MECHANISM AND VITALISM

Philosophical Aspects of Biology

Mechanism
and Vitalism

Philosophical Aspects of Biology

by

RAINER SCHUBERT-SOLDERN

Edited by

PHILIP G. FOTHERGILL, F.R.S.E.

Dept. of Botany, King's College, Newcastle upon Tyne

Foreword to the American Edition by

JAMES P. DOLL, C.S.C.

Lobund Institute, University of Notre Dame, Notre Dame, Indiana

UNIVERSITY OF NOTRE DAME PRESS • 1962

Notre Dame, Indiana

This translation of Philosophie des Lebendigen (*Verlag Styria, Graz*), was made by C. E. ROBIN

CONTENTS

Chapter   *Page*

Foreword to the American Edition   ix

Editor's Preface   xiii

Introduction   xv

I. THE EPISTEMOLOGICAL PROBLEM OF BIOCHEMISTRY   1
   1. Foundations of Knowledge   1
   2. Vitalism and Mechanism   10
     (a) *General Account*   10
     (b) *Development of the Position*   22
   3. Operational Field of Physico-chemical Laws   26
   4. Inanimate Wholes and the Principle of Stability   36
   5. Further Potentialities of Inanimate Matter   43

II. LAWS GOVERNING ANIMATE THINGS   46
   1. Animate and Inanimate Systems   46
     (a) *General Features*   46
     (b) *Life as a Source of Energy*   49
     (c) *Growth and Decay*   54
   2. The Principle of Instability   56
   3. What is living in the Organism?   57
   4. Order   62
   5. Biodynamic Wholeness   66

III. THE LIVING FORM   72
   1. The Problem of Morphogenesis   72
   2. Weismann's Germplasm Theory   73
   3. Epigenetic Theories   78
     (a) *Methodology*   78
     (b) *Oscar Hertwig's Theory of Biogenesis*   79
     (c) *Hans Driesch's Entelechial Wholeness Factor*   79
     (d) *Hans Spemann: Induction and Organizer*   85

(e) *Alexander Gurwitsch's Theory of an Embryo Field*   88
(f) *P. Weiss's "Field of Determination"*   88
(g) *The Gradient Theory of Boveri and Child*   89

IV. THE INDIVIDUALITY OF THE CELL   91
    1. The Cell as the Unit of the Living Form   91
    2. Nucleus and Cytoplasm as Functions of the Cell   96
    3. Gene and Genom   102
    4. The Cell as an Ordered Whole   108
    5. The Ordering of Cell Division   114

V. THE MULTICELLULAR ORGANISM   116
    1. The Relation of the Cell in the Cell Community 116
    2. The Multicellular Organism—a Colony of Protista?   118
        (a) *The Cell of the Multicellular Organism*   118
        (b) *The Ability of the Cells of Metabionts to live independently*   120
        (c) *The Merogenous Order of the Cell State* 121
    3. The Multicellular Organism as a Unit   126
        (a) *The Germ Cell and its Progeny*   126
        (b) *Purposiveness*   132
        (c) *Space-form and Time-form of the Metabiont*   134
        (d) *Antagonism between Unicellular and Multicellular Order*   137
    4. The Hierarchical Order of the Organic Form   141

VI. ADAPTATION AND REACTIVITY   149
    1. The Causal Order   149
    2. Ecological Adaptation   153
    3. Form as the Expression of Adaptation   162
    4. The Physiology of Stimulation   164
    5. The Biological Relevance of physiological Stimuli   170

VII. NORMS OF REACTION   175

   1. Protoplasmic Reactions   175
   2. Hormonal Reactions   177
   3. Reflex Actions   184
   4. Instinctive Actions   187
   5. Action Based on Experience   194
   6. Intelligent Action   201

VIII. LIFE'S ORDERED RELATIONSHIP   207

   1. Life's Ordered Relationship   207
   2. The Unity in Living Processes   209
   3. Immanence and Transcendence   213
   4. Wholeness   215
   5. *Forma corporis* as Final Cause   221
   6. *Ordo naturae* as End-Causality   224

BIBLIOGRAPHY   228

INDEX   236

FOREWORD TO THE AMERICAN EDITION

Recently George Beadle, the noted geneticist, Nobel prize-winner, and president of the University of Chicago, made this statement: "I see no conflict between science and religion. The answer to the question of creation still remains in the realm of faith. In early Biblical times . . . it was believed as a matter of faith that man was created as man. Since then, science has led us back through a sequence of evolutionary events in such a way that there is no logical place to stop . . . until we come to a primeval universe made of hydrogen. But then we ask, 'Whence came the hydrogen?' and science has no answer. Is it any less awe-inspiring to conceive of a universe created of hydrogen with the capacity to evolve into man than it is to accept the creation of man as man? I believe not." And any modern theologian and philosopher would agree with him.

The scientist may quibble with the hyperbole of "hydrogen" that is used, and the philosopher may dispute the statement that creation is a matter of "faith" rather than reason. But his point is well made, albeit in none-too-philosophical or scientific terms, which is excusable considering that he was talking to a convocation of Christian laymen. After all, this is the manner in which the accounts in the Bible are presented — *in modo non scientifice.*

Given a proper understanding of the distinction between primary and secondary acts of creation on the part of God and also between direct and indirect acts of creation, there are only two instances where a direct act of creation is absolutely necessary: first, when going from non-being to being (the primary act of creation), and secondly, when the intellectual soul is created. All other acts — including that of going from non-living to living — can be indirect acts of creation on the part of God. As a matter of fact, it is greater acclaim to the omnipotence of God that He operate by indirect causality rather than by direct intervention. The concepts of sustentative causality and Divine Providence are most beautifully illustrated by this mode of action. As Suarez says, "God does not interfere directly with the natural order, where secondary causes suffice to produce the intended effect."

Therefore, Beadle's statement could be rephrased in this manner: "Given the oneness of truth, it is conceivable that the first entity created by God could be a simple energetic force, convertible to matter which evolved through eons of time in a process of inorganic evolution, into organic matter, into living beings, through organic evolution, and up to man where another direct act of creation is demanded in going from non-intellectual to intellectual being." In this concept there is a continuum of truth from theology, through theodicy and ontology, to the philosophy of nature and on into the physical sciences which are the dialectical prolongations of the philosophy of nature. So whether a scientist works in the field of quantum mechanics, nuclear chemistry, paleontology, biology or what have you, there must be an unbroken concatenation of truth from the physical sciences to cosmological and theological concepts and vice versa.

However, the elision from a physical science to the philosophy of nature seems to be a "twilight zone" of truth in many instances. Most often it has been the scientist who projects his thinking into the philosophical sphere rather than the philosopher projecting his basic principles into the field of science. In *Mechanism and Vitalism* Schubert-Soldern seems to reach a happy medium between the two approaches. There are two unique features of this book: first of all, the author presents a wealth of biological data which must be accounted for by any philosophical consideration of life science; secondly, he presents an excellent and unbiased comparison of how the Mechanist and the Vitalist each attempts to correlate observed data with his philosophical system. Schubert-Soldern finds that neither alone is completely satisfactory and develops a "holistic" position — a position, however, leaning more toward vitalism than toward mechanism.

The last word by no means has been said on this question. But the author presents ideas that are most stimulating. His approach and his methods give particular impetus to the philosopher to approach biology from the philosophical point of view.

July 25, 1962   J. P. D.

EDITOR'S PREFACE

THIS book on theoretical biology by R. Schubert-Soldern, who is professor at the Vienna Institute for Experimental Zoology, Anatomy and Physiology, has been liberally edited and translated to suit English readers, who may not be very familiar with many of the ideas expounded. The author gives an account of mechanism and vitalism in which the treatment is partly historical and is brought up to date. There is particular reference to the works of experimenters like Driesch, Spemann and others, and an explanation is sought for the facts of biology, first through a mechanistic approach, and if this proves to be incomplete, a holistic interpretation is attempted. The author's position is probably best described as being holistic rather than merely vitalistic or mechanistic; he wishes to give an empirical basis to ideas in biology. The argument in the book thus often involves the use of concepts like teleology, entelechy, etc. To a theoretical biologist such ideas are commonplace, but to an experimentalist they may sound strange and rather odd. The author, however, uses many of these words in spite of their unfortunate English connotation because he does not wish to invent new technical terms. His "entelechy", for instance, has nothing to do with any ontological Platonic "idea"; he means rather the form or order producing wholeness in organisms. We hope that potential readers will not thereby be discouraged, because there is a wealth of constructive meaning involved in the proper use of the ideas which are ably expounded in this book.

P.G.F.

INTRODUCTION

OUR purpose in this book is to conduct a scientific enquiry into the nature of life. To do this, we must first be satisfied as to the sort of question to ask and then agree as to the sort of answer which will satisfy us.

In general we should be satisfied with an explanation which relates an unknown phenomenon with something previously truly known. In respect to life, however, there seems to be some doubt as to whether this aim is even a reasonable one. Is it possible to increase our knowledge by seeing a relationship between one natural phenomenon and another? The really crucial point of the discussion is whether biological processes are explicable in terms of what goes on at the inanimate level; in other words, whether life may be considered as completely within the range of physics and chemistry. The tacit assumption is made that the phenomena of inanimate nature are better known to us than those of a vital character. Does this imply that my own life is less well known to me than the contents of a test tube? Is it possible for me to know a mineral better than I know myself? It is from myself, from my conscious life, that I derive my awareness of the processes of nature. It is only in so far as they become evident to me, that they have existence or validity. It might, therefore, be said that all my knowledge and experience is derived from my analysis of my inner life, and from the discovery that particular objects in external nature display characteristics of my own life. In this case I should be justified in calling things living because they corresponded with what I knew of my own inner life.

In spite of all this, it is evident that this is not the way to put the question as to the nature of life. Our starting point would be based on an untenable theory of knowledge. The primary or ultimate phenomena of life or "Bios", in the biologist's use of the term, are objective. Our enquiry must begin from these and from these alone. Our attention must, then, be directed exclusively to observable phenomena. If we make phenomena our starting point, they must be accepted as such and be discussed within the sphere of experience in which they have been observed. It is therefore neither necessary nor permissible to attempt to explain these phenomena by means of experience derived from quite a different sphere, however exact and definite such other experience may be. We can only establish the nature of a thing by first making a thorough study of its characteristics. We can be sure we have found the really essential characteristics when we can show that each of them involves the existence of the rest. The characteristics will then be identical with the very nature of life, and will in fact be its expression.

Two methods of approach are available by which we can come to grips with the objective phenomena of life—generalization and induction. We must first establish that the manifestations of life in the many varieties of living creatures *are* truly and essentially manifestations of life. We must compare the life thus manifested with the phenomena of inorganic nature. Only thus is it possible to establish that living processes are of the same order as other natural processes, or are different from them. The method of exact inductive analysis of living phenomena cannot be separated from that of comparison. It is quite wrong to define these two methods as "generalizing" and "induction" respectively, and then to separate them as distinct, as A. Riehl (1908) did. Those who hold such views attribute "generalizing" to Aristotle and "induction" to Galileo[1] and Francis Bacon. The two methods were shown by Max Hartmann in 1933 to be sharply opposed. It is claimed by some that induction is a superior means of advancing knowledge. But Aristotle was familiar with induction even if he did not use the experimental method. After all, any comparison has to begin with an exact analysis of the particular

[1] See Lenard, 1937.

instance; induction is always necessary for making a generalization. On the other hand, if the universal validity of a conclusion made as a result of induction is to be established, the
conclusion must be shown by means of generalization and
comparison to have a wider applicability. Aristotle[2] used this
procedure. To exemplify its use the following question will
serve: what would be the significance of the Mendelian laws
if their application were restricted to *Mirabilis jalapa* or
Drosophila melanogaster? The two procedures, then, must
not be separated, still less opposed to each other. All the
same, the distinction is valuable in showing what is involved
in the examination of any natural phenomenon. The individual instance must first be established by experiment or
other form of particular research; the result must then be
compared with other results if it is to form the basis of a
formula of more general validity.

Our conclusion that the two procedures are inseparable
points to the fact that every experience which the inquiring
intellect has derived from its own inner life must be rigidly
excluded from the field of such scientific enquiry. The aspect
of nature which can be studied objectively falls within the
sphere of what the student may examine and experience. All
the knowledge and experience obtained in this sphere is
commensurable and so permits us to make comparisons. On
the other hand, everything taking its origin in the student's
inner life is derived from quite a different sphere of knowledge and is on a different plane. If this information is regarded
as objective fact, comparisons and assimilations will be made
which are quite inadmissible. Differences will appear which
will owe their origin entirely to the differences between the experience of the two spheres. Antinomies or contradictions
which are without logical foundation will turn up in respect of
one and the same objective situation. Something claiming to be
dialectic is smuggled into the natural world, something which
in reality is just the reflection of the genuine dialectic between

[2] See M. Hartmann, 1933.

the subject ego and the object: this is a fact explicitly and rightly emphasized by Erich Heintel.[3] The qualitative and quantitative expressions of the differences between various objects are irretrievably confused once this procedure is admitted—as it so often is.

Objective, observable facts alone can be the basis of any scientific theory of life. Even this limitation must be qualified, for feelings of warmth or cold are objectively ascertainable facts. It is the external world outside the observer and knowable through the senses which must form the basis of any scientific theory of life. In other words, biology treats of life as a phenomenon observable in objects knowable by means of the senses; it does not start from "I am alive". If a synthesis of these two points of view is to be achieved, it must be based upon the total specialized knowledge which biology can provide: the proofs used must be direct linear proofs, and cannot take the form of any genuine dialectic.

[3] 1944a and b.

1

THE EPISTEMOLOGICAL PROBLEM
OF BIOCHEMISTRY

1. FOUNDATIONS OF KNOWLEDGE

LIFE is something which we observe to be possessed in common by certain natural objects. To describe it we have to discover those qualities which are common to all animate things. It follows from this that no one object can be called "life". On the contrary, life is a phenomenon of which we become aware in various objects. We see animate things and we seek to know what all of them have in common. What have they that other bodies have not? Is life a principle of order? and, most important of all, is this principle of order something real? Is the name "living creature" a description of its essential nature? Or is it an order of things invented later by man and applied to something already existing, a category into which a number of natural objects are fitted in accordance with some arbitrary criteria? To answer this question, we shall have to survey briefly the path which leads from the subject observed to the enunciation of the general laws which describe it. We must at the same time indicate to what extent conclusions reached by this means are reliable.

What comes first and what is most direct and immediate is perception. How perception is defined in various philosophical systems does not at present concern us. This is the business of a theory of knowledge. So far as we are concerned, perception, with which every science begins, is the truest and most certain source of knowledge that can possibly exist. All natural science must begin with the liquid in the test tube, the tree before our eyes, the laboratory preparation which we examine. Natural science cannot immediately penetrate behind these direct observations. Does this immediate perception involve any knowledge of the thing perceived? No. All that is possible in the first instance is to describe what is perceived. Perception is the necessary basis for all subsequent knowledge: a thousand descriptions of perceptions may indeed give us knowledge of them, but certainly no knowledge which can be properly called scientific. The first step towards scientific knowledge is abstraction. The next question is whether the information obtained by means of abstraction from direct perception is any more truthful than the perception itself. If "No" is our answer, we have taken up the positivist standpoint, and we must give up all hope of further explanation. If we answer "Yes" our position is that of a realist.

If we take up the positivist position and deny all objective validity to the abstractions derived from perception, discussion is useless and science senseless. Everything beyond the description of perceptions is pure fairy tale. David Hume, for example, said that it is completely pointless to talk of "things in themselves". What we call a thing is nothing but a "bundle or collection of qualities". If qualities crop up repeatedly in the same combination, we give this conglomeration a name, but, as Hume said, we cannot make any valid statement about it, still less about the thing in itself. Is this theory admissible? The positivist claims that the only statements he can legiti- mately make are "Here is red, warm, smooth" and the like. But is not "Here is red" an abstraction—at least when I follow it with "There is red, too"? Once I identify "this red" and "that red", the perception or sensation loses something of its uniqueness. I have found something similar in "this" and "that", namely red; in a word I have already made an abstraction. If the positivist claims that the agreement of the two sensations is due to the likeness of the qualities perceived, he is himself abstracting the red quality from the sensation of reality as a whole. He must have done this already if he is to use the word "red" at all. Otherwise he could have said nothing but "here so"—quite apart from the fact that he cannot even say "here" without having the idea of location in space; this, too, is an abstraction, even if only a categorical abstraction.

Empirically there is no such thing as "here", or empty space in isolation. Even an extreme positivist is compelled to begin with abstractions.

To return to perception, to what is "here and now" perceived, let us for the moment leave the question whether the object is merely a set of qualities or the expression of a being which becomes manifest to us in its qualities. After perception comes memory (according to Erich Becher's [1925] statement of critical realism). This, positivism has never denied. Now memory (still according to Becher) is a source of certain truth. This fact is of decisive importance for us. If earlier perception, now retained in the mind by memory, is a foundation upon which knowledge may be built, it is possible to put various individual perceptions side by side and to test their correspondence with one another. The realization of this enables us entirely to ignore positivism in all our subsequent discussions. A comparison of the various perceptions enables us to detect a certain regularity in the recurrence of a bundle of qualities; from the presence of one of these qualities it is possible to infer the existence of all the others. In other words experience teaches us that a single quality never appears in isolation. It is this experience of regularity in what is presented to the senses which justifies the expectation, based on experience, that in the future everything will occur with the same regularity. It follows then that this regularity is one of the most reliable sources of all scientific knowledge. Were there any doubt about water boiling in normal circumstances at 100° Centigrade, or any doubt about the sun's setting and rising tomorrow morning, not only all natural science, but all human action and thought would be impossible.

We can speak of "laws of nature" because we are sure of this regularity. These laws are in fact nothing but expressions of this experience of regularity. Furthermore, the law of causality is something more than a sequence of events arbitrarily assumed to exist. Our assurance of regularity enables us to anticipate that one phase will be followed by another; because of this we readily assume causality and believe that in a particular instance we have a case of *propter hoc* as distinguished from *post hoc*. The essential distinction of *propter hoc* and *post hoc* is apparent from the moment we recognize in any one phase the conditions leading of necessity to the next. In science the distinction is brought home to us by way of experiments: a certain situation is artificially created and then the attempt is made to establish the regular consequences arising from arbitrary variations of the initial situation. It is this experience of regularity on which all biological pronouncements are based.

It is important that this should be linked with our earlier conclusion that every expectation of regularity involves an abstraction. A perception is unique and can never recur. If, however, any one perception permits of another's being foretold, this signifies that we have gone beyond the "here and now" of the individual perception. We do this as soon as a result is anticipated on the basis of the corresponding premisses. What is it that justifies this expectation of a result which can be foretold in advance? What is it that we abstract from the single case, and upon which attention is directed without regard to the individual case, and upon the basis of which a new situation may be expected? It is a definite "order" within which one case is in harmony with another. In so far as one situation may reasonably be expected to follow from another, this order contains implicit within itself that essential principle which is the cause of the second situation. It is an order in which two perceptions are related to one another; this same order establishes a causal dependence between the two perceptions. It is an order which we recognize in everything which gives us an experience of regularity. As Leo Gabriel expressed it, things happening with and after one another belong to the same order.

If we illustrate these facts with examples drawn from the field of biology, this principle becomes apparent in two ways. What, we may ask, justifies the assumption that the man standing before us has a heart with four chambers, two lungs and two kidneys? How do we know that he does not breathe

like an insect by means of tracheae, or in some way quite unknown to us? How do we know that he breathes at all? It is
only on the ground of our experience of regularity that we can
assume from a few visible features the existence of a complete
human bodily system. Every test in every particular case indicates that we can count upon it with absolute certainty. From
a single quality we can draw conclusions as to all the other
qualities. The fact that the one single quality is isolated is due
to some quality in us—the inadequacy of our sense perceptions, or the subjective standpoint we have chosen. It is untrue
that the qualities, though tied-up in "a bundle or collection",
are in fact just as separate as our own individual sensations.
To give an example—bright green reptiles do not as a rule
possess a green substance in their pigment cells. Under the
microscope, that which appears green is seen as yellow and
black, the two colours existing in separate cells. What then is
the reptile's colour—green, or black and yellow? The answer
is plain: the same quality appears as green to the naked eye
and as yellow and black under the microscope. It is at once
clear how idle it is to ask which is the more correct or truer
picture: the difference lies in the subjective standpoint of the
observer.

Thus whenever one quality enables us to infer with complete
regularity all the rest, we have before us but one thing; it can
be broken up into individual qualities, of course, but this
dissociation is arbitrary.

Besides the juxtaposition of the separate aspects of a natural
object, there is also an arrangement of these aspects as following one another. It is the regularity of their succession which
gives rise to that method of regarding nature which finds its
expression in the laws of nature. If we break up a natural
object into its individual qualities, and our experience of regularity enables us to see them as a unity, we have before us a
single factual whole; we can describe this whole and anticipate
it: but anything we do to it can only destroy it without ever
succeeding in actually isolating any of the individual qualities.
The most rewarding methods of enquiry have always been

those which have concentrated on variations in the object: not only are variations in what is presented to the senses noted and anticipated; the experimenter, by means of his experiment, himself takes a hand in the process. The experiment, too, anticipates a definite result. The experiment isolates the causal connections between the various phases of the changes taking place. It is well known that this, and no other, is the method of work in both physics and chemistry; to a substantial extent, this, along with the technique of morphological description, is the method of biology, too. Looked at in this way, the distinction between morphology and physiology is not one of subject but of method. It follows that, in spite of what is often stated in biological works, these two methods cannot be identified either with the generalizing induction of Aristotle or the exact induction of Galileo. The changes, recorded to begin with as they occur, and then repeated experimentally, are anticipated with the assurance that our experience of regularity gives us.

If our experience of regularity enables us to anticipate with certainty that, when substances *A* and *B* are brought together, the result will be *C* and *D*, this proves that there is something in *A* and *B* which actually causes substances *C* and *D*. All the criteria of chemistry are based on this principle. For example, when something burns with a yellow flame, or when it combines with chlorine to form common salt, or when it forms a caustic alkali on combining with water, and when it forms certain carbonates on combining with carbon dioxide, our experience of regularity assures us that in each case sodium must be present. The reactions are the tests for the presence of the substance. Chemistry recognizes substances by their reactions. In practice, in fact, one single characteristic reaction is accepted as a sign of the presence of a substance. If a substance behaves in the way one would regularly expect, this is an expression of its nature. In fact the only way a scientist can form conclusions as to the nature of anything is by assuming that the various changes that accompany and succeed one another express its nature and natural structure. If the substance always behaves as we expect it to, our certain expectation may be regarded as a law.

Thus the laws governing any substance are the expressions of its nature. I am entitled to expect that it will act in accordance with these laws. This being so, positivists are not entitled to say: "As soon as a number of laws appear in combination, we find a name for the natural object which presents them to our notice. The name and the name only—something applied arbitrarily—is what unites these various laws." In reality it is the certainty derived from our experience of regularity which proves to us that everything we perceive in a thing is integrated. Our means of recognition may be subjective, but the unity of all the distinguishing marks is not. In his *Integral Logic*, Gabriel (1949b) established a logical principle which forms the only possible foundation for any knowledge of nature. We have, we think, established the principle that the properties inherent in a being constitute a unity; not merely this, however, but also that regularities, properties and subjective experiences—all things in fact which express its inner structure—form a single entity.

All we need to show now is that the simultaneously co-existing properties and the succession of phases both join in expressing the same real nature. Once these phenomena are properly related the nature of the object has been discovered.

Abstractions have been several times mentioned, and we have established that the certainty given by our experience of regularity gives us the right to make abstractions. By divesting perception of its uniqueness we arrived by abstraction at a comparison which, in turn, led us to a recognition of regularity. By this means knowledge of the nature of an object has become possible. Thus, for example, it is possible to make an abstraction from this and that particular lime tree of the qualities which make them lime trees, and confidently to expect, through our experience of regularity, the presence of roots and sieve tubes in our specimen—and this in spite of the fact that the tree is standing in the garden and nobody has ever seen its roots or sieve tubes. Such predictions are possible because of the order in which the individuals are integrated as members of a class. This being the case, one can progress from the lime tree to flowering plants in general, from them to all plants, and finally to living creatures in general as one goes on making successive abstractions. One can go even further and bring together everything that can be said about material objects in general; even here there is the possibility of a real integration, even if only a conceptual one. Once we have seen a material object and are assured of its extension in space our experience of regularity makes us no less assured of the fact that it has weight. Now if we want to know what life is, the first thing we have to do is to make up our minds whether, by means of abstraction, we can affirm anything common to all living creatures which is not shared by other material things. A table certainly shares with living creatures a corporeal nature; what qualities does the table lack whose absence entitles us to say that it is inanimate?

There are two possibilities. Living creatures might have their place within the material order and life then might simply represent a special case among the general laws governing material things. In this case the same forces would operate in both living creatures and inanimate matter. At most there might be certain combinations of forces, common to all living creatures, which are in principle indistinguishable from the phenomena of inanimate matter. On the other hand it is conceivable that living creatures belong to an order of things quite distinct from that of inanimate objects.

The first of these explanations is that provided by the mechanistic theory. Vitalism, on the other hand, takes the view that in living beings a radically different principle is operative. Before examining these theories more closely we must decide what the phenomena are, which are characteristic of all living creatures. The common element must be discovered before we can argue about it. For example, what is the quality which a fungus shares with a stag but not with a stone? In outward appearances it looks more like a stone than a stag. It is true that in the higher plants, in insects and in vertebrates, we find tube systems such as vascular bundles, tracheae and blood-vessels; yet these tell us nothing, for they are constituted in quite different ways, are formed of quite different materials and perform quite different functions. Of course, one point does strike us: all three tube systems serve to move materials from one place to another; they are all directed to a definite purpose. This may be a kind of indication, but it does not take us very far, because many living creatures have nothing of the sort to show. Passing into the sphere of the microscopic, we find one form-element—the cell—recurring everywhere, and to a large extent in the same form always. Nevertheless it is difficult even here to give an unambiguous picture of the nature of life. The contents of the cell are fluid, probably colloidal, and fluids and colloids are familiar things in inanimate nature. However hard we seek, we can never find a single definite form which is characteristic of all living things.

If, on the other hand, we examine the processes which go on in living creatures we find three characters common to them all. All of them exhibit (a) metabolism, (b) change of form, and (c) irritability. When these three phenomena are apparent, they are sure signs that life exists, and may in consequence be called the "life-phenomena". Another characteristic of all living creatures is "adaptation to environment".

Life, therefore, is not something that can be examined in isolation; living things are not a special category of corporeal objects; definite processes occur in certain bodies, and these bodies have the peculiarity of adapting themselves to their environment. The four vital phenomena we have mentioned are found nowhere outside bodies, but we can compare them with one another and point out common features by abstracting from single instances. What distinguishes the vital phenomena as such is that a body is at one time alive, at another—though present completely as far as material is concerned—lifeless. To understand life we must contrast it with death. The characteristic features of vital phenomena—metabolism, change of form, irritability and adaptation to environment—

lead the vitalist to claim life as something existing in its own right. The exponent of the mechanistic theory is therefore constrained to show that they are capable of a purely physical explanation. These phenomena are entirely objective in character. No statement made about them can have any value as a source of knowledge, unless it is derived from purely objective sources. Two consequences follow from this.

1. Every statement we are entitled to make must be based on sense experience. The essential quality which is open to biological research must always be examined empirically, and must not lose contact with sense experience. All purely conceptual ideas, all that cannot be immediately perceived, must be shown to have been arrived at purely by abstraction from direct experience. Biology is limited to the field which is bounded on the one hand by direct perception, on the other by the experience of regularity.

2. Dualistic views are not admissible unless they can be proved lineally upon this one level of knowledge. Any set of ideas explicitly drawn from the sphere of subjective experience must necessarily lead to a false dualism existing only in the sphere of dialectic and detached from all scientific truth. This reasoning ends in a nominalist agnosticism.

2. VITALISM AND MECHANISM

(a) *General Account*

Life, the subject matter of biology, is a phenomenon intimately connected with matter. Biology, therefore, must be concerned with the relationship between matter and the phenomenon we call life. Animate and inanimate things have matter in common, and it is in their materiality that the two can best be compared. In this comparison, two theories, vitalism and mechanism, compete for the mastery. The vitalist sees in a living organism the convergence of two essentially different factors. For him matter is shaped and dominated by a life principle; unaided, matter could never give rise to life. The mechanist, on the other hand, denies any joint action of two essentially different factors. He holds that matter is capable of giving rise to life by its own intrinsic forces. The mechanist considers matter to be "alive". The vitalist considers that something immaterial lives in and through matter. These two opposing views were known even in ancient times; they formed the basis of the differences between Aristotle and Democritus on this subject.

Aristotle did not maintain a special status for living things different from lifeless matter. The multiplicity of substantial forms in which he believed involved a corresponding multiplicity in the peculiar qualities characterizing the various things. What Aristotle said about life, he held to be equally applicable to all corporeal objects. The common element in all things is matter; matter is presupposed as the foundation of every corporeal object; it is present everywhere but never appears in an unformed state. It is through the form that matter receives its special characteristics in each particular case; everything is made up of matter and form, *hyle* and *morphe*. As matter is always perceived as possessing a definite form one may reasonably ask how matter and form can be two principles in reality distinct from one another. The views of the physical world current in ancient times enabled an answer to be given to this question. For example, when water evaporates and becomes vapour, the same substratum clearly takes upon itself two different forms. There is something constant which was at first water and then vapour; it is this constant factor which is called matter. The difference between water and water vapour is such as to indicate that there are two different "forms"; these distinct "forms" are imprinted upon the same underlying "matter". This underlying matter is thus a reality, and Aristotle called it *materia prima*; form as such is called *forma substantialis*. As soon as the *materia prima* receives the imprint of any such form and so loses its previous unformed condition, it appears as *materia secunda*. This, presented to us again in particular objects, takes on the character of *materia signata*. Although the argument is here based on a false scientific hypothesis, a large number of scholars hold Aristotle's theory of hylomorphism. (They do not, of course, hold it in respect of the changing condition of aggregates.) Gredt (1946) pointed to the process of nutrition as an example of the truth of hylomorphism. The material which has its form as food is absorbed by an organism and becomes a constituent of the organism's own form: when this occurs one can accept a real change of form: the underlying substance, formerly food and now a part of the organism's body, represents the *materia prima*. Thomas Aquinas made Aristotle's hylomorphism the keystone of the philosophy of his *Summa*. Hylomorphism was incorporated into the natural philosophy of the Thomist school. It has been energetically championed in recent times from the biological standpoint, in particular by Andre (1931, 1947). In opposing this biological point of view Mitterer (1947) pointed out that the image underlying hylomorphism is that of a craftsman. The craftsman can make all sorts of objects from one and the same material (*materia prima*): the idea in his mind of the object to be made (which can be multiplied as often as desired) corresponds to the *forma substantialis*. Further, the variety of objects which can be imprinted upon the same material corresponds to the variety of substantial forms. Furthermore a potter, for example, can make a similar vase out of the most different materials. Just as the potter can make many different vessels out of the same clay, the most varied ideas or conceptions find expression in the same material. The clay is anthropomorphically made the image of the *materia prima* of nature.

A further conception is of importance to us. A new form can be imprinted upon matter already having a form: the matter thus loses the form it had previously—a *privatio* occurs. Thus, when a plant builds itself up with air and mineral salts, it deprives these substances of their form and imposes upon them its own form. The material substance loses the forms of carbon dioxide or mineral salt and takes on the form of the plant. Similarly, a snake eats a mouse: the snake deprives the material substance of the mouse of its form and impresses upon the substance the form of its own body.

If we use this terminology, the form must be the cause of

the vital phenomena exhibited by the living creature. The phenomena are the expression of the form, which employs the matter as the field of its operation. Whatever objections may be brought forward against hylomorphism, it may be made acceptable to the modern mind if the *forma substantialis* is defined as the principle of order. In this case, the plant or snake in the examples given would be the principle of order to which the material substance belongs. In any case, the material substance must be shewn clearly to be capable of receiving any sort of form, and the "form" as in some sense real and distinct. So understood, hylomorphism does not express the distinctive nature of life as a form-principle: no new principle is superimposed upon matter other than that which was in essence already present in lifeless things. *Hyle* and *morphe* are the joint constituents in every material object, whatever its nature. We can look for the distinctive character of life only in any quality which distinguishes animate forms from inanimate ones. In so far as modern vitalism assumes some immaterial force in the living thing which works upon lifeless matter, it accepts hylomorphism but admits it only in the case of living things. Most vitalists, in disagreement with Aristotelianism, believe that in the sphere of lifeless matter, matter functions automatically without the intervention of any non-material factor. This automatically-functioning matter has in any case already received its form and, as conceived by most vitalists, does not correspond to the Aristotelian *materia prima*.

On the other hand, Democritus held that matter itself produces animate things. To him all natural processes are no more than phenomena of correlation between atoms. His view, however, differs from that of modern mechanistic theories in that he based the variety we see in nature upon a variety in the structure of matter itself. Matter is built up of atoms of different character, and the variety of material things is produced by differing combinations of these various kinds of atoms. To Democritus life was nothing but a particular operation of the atoms, yet it is interesting to note that he postulated the existence of a special sort of "soul atom": it is "soul atoms" which give rise to life. Democritus agrees with the exponents of modern mechanistic theories in holding that life is due to the operation of atoms in combination, but his "soul atoms", although corporeal, testify by their special character that life is in some way self-sufficient and that it exists in its own right. Life may be a purely material phenomenon, but it can be produced only by a special sort of matter.

Although the opposition between the vitalists and the mechanists is not the same as that between Aristotle and Democritus, Aristotle is rightly regarded as the father of all vitalist views and Democritus of all mechanistic ones. It is from Aristotle that vitalism derives its conception of an active and essentially immaterial factor dominating matter, even though it accepts this relation only in respect of the world of life and rejects it in respect of inanimate things. Mechanistic theories regard life as a meeting place of a large number of atomic constituents; these same constituents, in correlation with one another, produce all the phenomena of both animate and inanimate nature. As already mentioned, there are two important concepts yet to be examined. Democritus regarded matter as consisting of atoms. Apart from atoms nothing exists. All phenomena, therefore, connected with matter, can derive from no other source than from the forces residing in the atoms. This is essentially the point of view of chemistry. If other factors are to be admitted, factors which are clearly energy and nothing else, and which operate as such upon matter, these, as Bavink said (1927–9, 1954), belong to the realm of physics. Until recently this was the general view, and it persists to some extent even now. The opposition between the concepts of energy and of matter was brought to an end only by Einstein's theory of relativity and by developments in atomic physics. Matter is now reduced to energy because it can be measured in terms of energy. The smallest components of the atom can be understood in mechanical terms as waves, and can be evaluated as the operational centres of definite mechanical systems expressed in physical terms. This microstructure of matter found expression in Moritz Schlick's (1925) laws of microphysics. Thus from Democritus to modern times runs a continuous line of thought. Matter is regarded as having a granular structure, whether the granules are material grains or fields of energy, whether the granular components are the atoms of Democritus, the invisible atoms of the eighteenth and nineteenth centuries, or the nuclear components with opposite electrical charges known to twentieth-century atomic physicists. Living things, too, are considered to be nothing but the effects of the interaction of these granular components. Life, therefore, can be defined as the sum of the combined operations of the granular components of matter.

The opposing energy centres arising in such systems interact with one another; the result is an organism which we can regard as ordered. The order, however, is based upon the operation of the granular components when they come together, and arises only when they do so. The principle of order is immanent in the components by their very nature. In this view the principle of the organism is that of a system made up of parts: following Hans Driesch (1928a, 1938), we can call it a "merogenous" principle.

According to Aristotle, on the other hand, the living creature can be understood only when viewed as a whole: its nature is determined only as a whole. The word "organism" is indeed the classical technical term for something which consists of parts but in which the parts have no independent existence until they are brought together and united in due order in the organism. In the organism the part derives its existence only from the whole. It is not the parts which give rise to the whole but the whole which gives rise to the parts. The organism is divided into parts as the body into limbs. Mechanistic theories, on the other hand, have divested the living organism of its character as a principle of wholeness and unity. The organic character of the structure of a living being has been widely questioned. For this reason the concept of "wholeness" has recently taken the place of the concept of "organism". Today "wholeness" has become a synonym for the classical "organism" of philosophy, while "organism" is now used simply as a concrete term for a living creature. The principle of wholeness is seen in the grouping of all the parts or all the partial processes round a centre; the part is capable of existing only with reference to the whole. The order of the whole precedes the effectiveness of the parts. Following Driesch (1928a, 1938) we may call the principle making for wholeness a "hologenous" principle.

The problem of the nature of the laws governing life confronted us at the very outset with the question of how life is related to the material substance in which it manifests itself. This is generally speaking the starting point of any argument in favour of a mechanistic theory. If a book begins with chemistry, it usually ends with a mechanistic conclusion. On the other hand vitalists, such as Hans Driesch (1928a) and most of those who follow him, make the problems of form, or the phenomena of morphogenesis, the starting point of their argument. Jakob von Uexküll (1920) started from the physiology of stimuli and adaptation. As we shall see, not even Driesch (1928a) believed it possible to prove the autonomy of life by chemical means. Morphologists and developmental physiologists consider the form and detect in morphogenesis a process of development apparently inconsistent with all mechanistic speculations.

If the form as such is to be regarded as the foundation of all life-processes, it must follow that this factor can be shown as operative even in the purely chemical processes within the organism. For if a completely different principle is introduced into the normal chemical and physical processes, this new principle must surely make its presence known by some change in the course of the chemical processes. These processes, however, do not differ substantially from those in the inorganic sphere. If the final result can be shown to be of a distinctive character, the arrangement of things at the beginning, the starting-point, must also be different from that in the inorganic sphere. Gustav Wolff (1935) insisted most emphatically that this is the case. Alexis Moyse (1948) also stressed the difference in the starting-points in the organic and inorganic spheres. These two scholars have no intention, as vitalists, of abandoning the field of biochemistry to the mechanists. The thoroughly consistent standpoint of Hedwig Conrad-Martius (1944) differs somewhat from that of these two. A comparison of the three standpoints shows how they supplement one another.

Gustav Wolff's (1935) starting point was the experimental physiology of development. He disagreed with Driesch (1928) in regarding as the most striking distinguishing mark of life the way in which it is determined by the ultimate goal or purpose towards which it tends: the purposiveness in terms of which he defined wholeness and life generally. Hence the chemical processes of life can run their course only in so far as they are controlled by the ultimate purpose. Moyse (1948) laid the stress on the starting point. He allowed the chemical laws their full sway. But the chemical processes start from a situation which differs from those of inanimate nature. Furthermore, the power of the organism to control its own behaviour is a factor influencing the chemical processes quite independently of the chemical and physical processes which are at work. The concept of form and the experiments of Driesch (1941) and Spemann (1936) in the field of developmental physiology constituted the point of departure for Hedwig Conrad-Martius (1944). In her opinion, however, it was totally unnecessary to give up the idea of an autonomous life process in favour of Driesch's chemical reactions. According to her, the life principle affects even the molecular structure. Molecules which are the components of a living organism receive a fundamentally and radically different form under the influence of a formative entelechy that is directly suited to its bodily nature. In a sense, therefore, life itself produces the building materials which are its bases, through this formative entelechy. Only through the operation of an additional factor, the entelechy of its existence, is the total organism built up from the raw materials of its structure. For her therefore the mechanistic contention that living beings consist of the same materials as

minerals was wholly false. This amounts to an *a priori* rejection
of all mechanistic argument. Of those who accept without
qualification the validity of chemistry in the biological sphere,
we are left with Gustav Wolff (1933 and 1935) and Alexis
Moyse (1948), but these two brought biochemistry within the
sphere dominated by life.

If we ignore these three very gifted thinkers, it would seem
that the problem of life can be attacked only from the point
of view of the phenomenon taken as the starting point. The
phenomena of life seem to present a dualism or a diametrical
opposition. This was indeed the view of both Driesch (1941)
and Neuberg (1944). If we begin with morphogenesis, we
arrive at vitalism; if we begin with chemistry we arrive at a
mechanistic explanation. Have we here a dialectic in Pasqual
Jordan's (1935, 1949) sense? His idea was that both conclusions are correct, that it is merely a question of the angle
from which the problem is attacked. Jordan compares the
different views to the undulatory and corpuscular theories of
light. But, as Heintel (1944a and b) pointed out, this view
is untenable inasmuch as here the only opposites which are
acceptable are those which can be treated in the dialectical
manner. Unless one accepts a dialectic in this sense, however, one is more or less obliged to despair of finding a consistent explanation of the life principle. Are we then forced
to believe, as Driesch suggested, that the living organism consists of a vitally controlled "planning office" and a laboratory
working automatically on mechanistic principles?

Those who, like von Bertalanffy (1932, 1949), Dürken
(1925a and b) and, to some extent, Mittasch (1938), support
the theory of wholeness, take up a rather different standpoint.
They attempt a kind of synthesis between vitalism and mechanism, in the hope of reconciling two conclusions reached by
researchers in two different spheres. It is the teaching of
physiological chemistry that the organism is wholly built up
of chemical molecules; in consequence it results from the
forces immanent in these molecules. On the other hand, the
physiology of development indicates that these molecules con-

stitute a single unit, and that as generation succeeds generation this unitary construction continues to be reproduced. So Bertalanffy (1932, 1949) concluded that a true whole does not exist but that it is built up only of the particles which comprise it. The forces immanent in the particles maintain themselves in a state of fluid equilibrium which together must be more than the sum of the parts in the whole. If this is the case, the constituents of living things are the forces of inorganic nature and it is not very obvious why Bertalanffy repudiated mechanism. Mechanists have never maintained more than that life consists in a correlation of the operations of the atomic particles. How are we to understand "organic" or "wholeness" except as terms for a special combination of physical forces? Mittasch (1938) believed that the whole is produced by a firm cohesion of the particles. Every level of particle, the atom for instance, is in many ways determined in particular by its inner structure; but in their possible powers of combination particles are free. While the formation of a molecule determines the freedom of the particles, the resultant superior units (molecules) acquire new possibilities which in their turn await determination. One of these levels of determination is the living organism. This, too, seems quite possible to me; within certain limits it can be shown to correspond with facts. All the same, I do not see why this theory should not be regarded as a variety of mechanism.

The question now arises whether a composite entity can be anything more than the sum of its parts. This could be the case only if the whole acted in accordance with laws different from those governing the parts in isolation. It is the old question, whether in chess the queen is worth more than a rook and a bishop. The queen can do only what the rook and the bishop can do; yet the queen is more valuable than a rook and a bishop because she combines the powers of both. In the "wholes" as understood by von Bertalanffy the atomic forces are united in an organic whole. All the same they are the only forces present just as in chess the queen's powers are but a combination of the separate powers of rook and bishop. Von

3

Bertalanffy's (1932, 1949) "whole" is nothing but a sum of multiple components in the manner of the queen in chess. A comparison of this view with that of Mittasch (1938) will show that they are essentially different, although both theories are mechanistic in character.

For when the electrical charges of two particles are neutralized by their coming together in a higher entity, they no longer exist. The newly-formed entity no longer exhibits the positive and negative charges which the constituent particles had before their combination; new laws appear, different from those applicable to the particles. If then a living organism represents a definite level in the hierarchy of free and determinate existences in Mittasch's (1938) sense, it must follow that it does not exhibit simply the sum of the physical laws applicable to its molecules, any more than the molecule exhibits simply the sum of the atomic laws, or the atom those of the nucleus and the electrons. Is this a "whole" in the same sense as the classical concept of an organism? Undoubtedly it is. Nevertheless this "whole" is not quite the Aristotelian "organism", since it is the parts which constitute the organism. We have to do, therefore, with a "whole" which, as defined above, rests upon a merogenous principle. Hence hologenous systems, "wholes", are conceivable which are constituted merogenously and which therefore rest upon merogenous principles. Yet there might well exist Aristotelian "wholes" which are not only hologenous systems but are also constituted by hologenous factors. To avoid misunderstanding I must explain what I mean by a "hologenous system". A system is "hologenous" or "whole" when it presents itself to us as a complete whole independently of whether it became a whole through a multiplicity of efficient causes or only a single one. While, according to Driesch (1928a), "wholes" can only rest upon hologenous principles.

In consequence we have before us the following purely theoretical possibilities:

(i) A merogenous system consisting of parts, which is nothing but the sum of the laws operating in the parts and which rests upon a merogenous principle.

(ii) A hologenous system, a whole which is nevertheless based upon a merogenous principle. The forces inherent in the parts generate a whole; but the whole is an agglomeration of particles and becomes whole, hologenous, through the operation of the particles.

(iii) A hologenous system, a whole which is constituted by a hologenous principle. Here the principle is a whole which produces a complete entity from its parts; by themselves, however, the parts could never produce a whole.

In order to avoid yet another misunderstanding, we must make clear what we mean by "sum". We are always being told, quite rightly, that the sum is itself a whole. All the same the idea of sum necessarily implies something "merogenous". The word "sum", therefore, represents an aspect under which the mind creates a unity out of a multiplicity. The process of synopsis amounts to practically the same thing as summing-up. I grasp mentally twenty separate apples as a "sum" of apples. If I have a certain number of molecules in a test-tube, I regard all that goes on there as the sum of all the separate reactions taking place. Thus the word "sum" implies merely the mental combination of the parts irrespective of whether there is any real connection between them. In speaking of a "sum" of effects, therefore, we simply mean that single things or phenomena are "lumped together" mentally.

This gives some idea of what we can expect of a view of life based on chemistry. In this case the problem of life must be treated from a purely chemical point of view irrespective of any morphogenetic aspects, and must ignore the experiments of Driesch (1928a), or Spemann (1936). Biochemistry represents a point of view at least as important as that of morphogenesis. As living and non-living things are composed of the same chemical constituents, the object of biochemical experiments must be to establish the relationship between the chemical processes taking place within animate things and those of inanimate nature. If they are identical, the decision must favour mechanism, and arguments in favour of vitalism must then be sought in a completely different field: they would, however, tell against a completely vitalistic viewpoint—against that of Driesch, for instance. It would be necessary to accept in life a dualism, or two separate principles, and this dualism, as Driesch seemed to believe, would extend even to the physiological sphere. Furthermore, if the result of enquiries leads us to believe that living beings are wholes composed of merogenous, in this case molecular, principles the decision would similarly have to be given in favour of mechanism, even if the wholes could be discovered only in the domain of life. For, as Max Hartmann said (1933) logically and with complete justification, it is the peculiarity of a certain combination which makes life unique. A decision between vitalism and mechanism is unavoidable and there is, I therefore conclude, no *via media* between them. In my opinion, this decision is best reached in the field of chemistry. For chemical processes are plain, and the principles of chemical reactions are not easily misunderstood. We have, therefore, to explain what life is, if it is regarded simply as a chemical process.

(b) *Development of the Position*

The establishment of the fact that visible matter consists of a limited and fixed number of elements and that all material objects are made of a single element or of a combination of two or more elements was of decisive importance for our ideas about life. It became evident that there is no elemental difference between animate and inanimate matter; the elements composing both are identical. In fact, the very meaning of the word element underwent a change. Elements were no longer considered to be fields of operation which were given structure and shape by substantial forms: instead the elements themselves were thought to be the ultimate basic substances defying further analysis, and by their combinations the world is built up. The forces which brought about the combination of the elements one with another were present in the elements themselves; it was possible to be certain of their presence at all times. Once the element was shown to be elementary, its activity was necessarily expressive of its innermost nature, and chemical reactions were thus entirely the result of the essential properties of the elements, of their affinities for one another following definite laws of valency. This conception made it quite unnecessary to assume the existence of any non-material factor, such as substantial form. For all that we can see happening in matter can be seen as the result of the operation of forces residing in the matter. Thus nothing outside matter provokes the activity of the material which in itself is passive; the material is itself operative, active. Thus the whole concept of matter was changed: matter was no longer a mass waiting to be fashioned, it was seen to consist of active grains in correlation. Hence, matter bears within itself the efficient cause of chemical action. The cause is immanent in the matter, and does not transcend it as formerly thought.

If metaphysical conclusions are drawn from these facts, a materialist view of reality becomes an obvious consequence. About 1800, however, the metaphysics of materialism received a decided check from vitalism, a check reinforced later by Johann Muller, the founder of modern physiology. The "vitalism" as usually considered without qualification was actually based upon the newly acquired knowledge of matter.

It is true that animate and inanimate matter are composed of the same elements. But what was thought to be important was the relation between two sorts of compound formed from these elements and their relation to life. Living organisms always consist of organic compounds, never of inorganic ones alone. Moreover, organic compounds which are not contained in an organism, are clearly always of organic origin. Again, we often see inorganic compounds arising from organic ones through the disintegration of dead organisms or as the waste products of living ones. Nowhere in nature, however, do we see the opposite process at work; inorganic chemical compounds do not give rise to organic ones. If the forces at work in inorganic nature are always bound up with atoms and molecules, and if these of themselves can never produce organic compounds, it must follow that the inorganic forces by themselves are incapable of forming anything organic. But if inorganic compounds are formed by the decay of organic matter, it is clear that the inorganic forces reappear as soon as the elements can react freely—as soon as they are freed from some sort of bond or fetter laid upon them by the organism. From this we may conclude that organic compounds arise not simply from the elements, but only through the operation of life; the inorganic forces are insufficient of themselves to build up organic compounds. The contention of the vitalist, then, was founded upon this fact.

If the elements by themselves, even when present in the right proportions, are incapable of producing organic compounds, some additional factor must exist which elevates them to the organic level. This factor is present only in living things; it is life itself. This factor cannot be material in character, for material things consist only of those elements which by themselves cannot produce life. It must be an immaterial factor which moulds materials like a force. It must be the life-force.

We see, then, that the uniqueness of life was thought to be a corollary of the uniqueness of organic matter, and that organic matter was itself a visible manifestation of life. This idea of an immaterial factor transcending the elements served to restore the Aristotelian entelechy, and reasserted that principle of order which is opposed to the matter consisting of elementary particles. I want to remind you once more that the vitalists' proof of the presence of the life-force was the inability of the inorganic elements to produce organic compounds. These compounds set up an impassable barrier between the organic and the inorganic, and so gave chemistry its two divisions, which were in principle independent. It was held, too, that if it were ever possible to produce organic from inorganic matter, the barrier would be broken and the argument would be invalid.

In 1828 the barrier did in fact fall. Wöhler succeeded in making urea, a purely organic compound, from inorganic materials. Hitherto urea had only been known to occur in, or had been obtained from, living organisms. This epoch-making discovery created an entirely new situation. The concept of a life-force now became superfluous because the gulf between organic and inorganic had been bridged, and thus life was robbed of its uniqueness. If the elements possess the power of producing organic compounds, and these constitute the specific character of life, life as actual is preformed in the potentialities of inorganic matter. As time went on more and more organic compounds were made artificially and each was a further disproof of life's uniqueness. The molecular structure of organic compounds, however, remained unknown until Kekulé (1859) demonstrated the power of carbon atoms to form chains. Our knowledge of the structure of carbohydrates and fats was thus extended. The fact that it was for a long time impossible to synthesize albumin played no small part in theoretical disputations about the mysterious albumin molecule which we meet in the scientific literature at the turn of the century. This molecule is important in the process of assimilation. At length Emil Fischer (1901) succeeded in proving that polymeric albumins were composed of numerous amino-acids of high molecular weight. The production of organic compounds by molecular and atomic forces was at last completely explained by physiologists when they showed that in nutrition certain amino-acids were equivalent to albumin. It was shown that under certain circumstances albumin was not sufficient for the nutrition of a child. To be sufficient, it had to contain eight distinct amino-acids. Suitable albumin, therefore, must contain these specific amino-acids. A significant fact resulting from these discoveries was that Schwann (1839) and Schleiden (1833) believed they had found the physical element of life in the cell. Schwann enquired whether the totality of life governed the growth and development of the cell units, or whether the organism was itself determined by the collaboration of the primary cellular forces. He favoured the second alternative. We must remember that he regarded cells as physical elements. For Schwann and his successors the discovery of the cell was a definite proof of mechanism. But the cell proved to be something other than its discoverers expected. Even if the cell remains the morphological unit of life, it possesses already, to the fullest extent, all the complications of an animate thing. The manifold problems of the organism are not explained by simple physical formulae, simply because the organism can be divided up into cells. When the view of von Siebold (1845) and Dujardin (1841) that protozoa, and in particular infusoria, were unicellular organisms, proved correct, every possibility of regarding the cell as the physical unit of life disappeared. The cell itself proves to be highly complicated, to be once more an organism. Efforts have been made to divide cells into their ultimate components: in these efforts almost every structural particle has been made the starting point of some theory or other. We shall meet with these ideas frequently later in this book.

In any case it has been established that organic compounds can be synthesized starting with inorganic materials. It is also clear that the cells and the organism as a whole are made up of such materials exclusively. It is true that a large number of compounds important in living matter have not as yet been synthesized and their composition is still unknown. Nevertheless, it seems clear enough that the same physical and chemical forces which go to form inorganic compounds are at work in the synthesis of these complicated and comparatively gigantic molecules. As I have already said, vitalism is based on quite different considerations, and in the new form given to it by Hans Driesch (1928a, 1938) the theory remains unshaken by this newly-acquired knowledge.

3. OPERATIONAL FIELD OF PHYSICO-CHEMICAL LAWS

In all natural processes involving change, the physicist sees phenomena of movement induced by some potential. Are we justified in assuming that anything different is occurring in living matter? The endeavour to give a uniform explanation to natural phenomena demands a principle to which all material processes are subjected. Since Wöhler (1828) broke down the barrier between the organic and the inorganic, there is no longer any reason to erect a barrier between physics and biology.

The fundamental character of a natural object may be expressed by the statement that "everything is defined by the laws which govern it". In all our future discussions this must be our criterion. The logical principles set forth at the beginning of this chapter must for the moment be left on one side; we must concentrate now on the laws which govern nature. If two things are governed by the same laws, their essential structure is identical; if the laws governing them are different, their natures are different, too. There can be no canon of difference or identity other than this. All that we observe is an expression of the laws governing the object. It is by his tests that a chemist, for instance, determines the nature of a substance. What, for example, is chlorine? A substance which, when pure, is a yellowish gas. With silver nitrate it produces a white precipitate which is soluble in ammonia. If atomic weight and all its reactions tally, we conclude that all these characteristics are integrated in the substance under observation. All that we observe, directly or indirectly, is an expression of the laws governing the object and inherent in it.

A further consequence follows. Some natural objects, which can be broken up into their parts or which we can observe being formed from their separate parts, exhibit no qualities other than the sum of the qualities inherent in the parts. Such an object has no character of its own. What character it has is that of the parts which compose it. For example, water in a glass has no other characteristic than those of all the separate molecules of water added together. It makes no difference whether the parts are like or unlike one another. We can call such an aggregate as water in a glass a merogenous system; it is based on a merogenous system, a multiplicity of partial principles.

Wöhler (1828) and many others synthesized organic compounds by bringing together in the appropriate order atoms originating in the inorganic world. This suggests that the molecule of organic matter owes its essential structure to the combined operation of the forces in the atoms. For molecules consist of nothing but atoms. If then the difference between animate and inanimate was equivalent to the difference made by chemists between organic and inorganic, life became explicable in purely physical terms as soon as chemists synthesized the first organic compound. The argument proceeds as follows: As a molecule results from the presence and combination of atoms, the atoms, i.e. the forces immanent in them, are primary to the molecule which is derived from them. The molecule, inorganic or organic, is explicable in terms of atoms, is the sum of its atoms. Life, too, then, is no more than a correlation of atomic forces. Thus must run any explanation which seeks to explain a phenomenon solely as the result of another phenomenon.

If we regard the structure of a living organism as nothing but a compound of elements, it appears that such elements are potentially capable of building up not merely molecules of organic compounds but also complete organisms. Chemical analysis reveals the existence of these elements and nothing else. These elements, these atoms, then must be the constituents of organisms. But it then becomes clear what, essentially, biological phenomena are. All the changes in inorganic nature are due to the potentialities of the atoms; the processes of life no less are simply highly complicated correlations of similar atomic processes. We must look for the source of life, then, in these processes.

In inorganic nature inorganic compounds are simple and stable. It is true that a certain amount of change and decay occurs, but the stable compounds of the inorganic world can in general exist side by side undisturbed. Strong acids and gases with electrical affinities have no enduring existence in nature, as they would be immediately neutralized. To speak colloquially, the compounds "mind their own business" and so endure. If a chemical disturber of the peace arises the changes to which it gives rise are simple in character and tend to a new state of equilibrium. The compounds of high molecular weight in a living organism seem to behave quite differently. There we find the various compounds continuously at work one upon the other. They are brought together in close compass and are of their nature unstable. Their existence is constantly threatened by the attacks of free oxygen and of enzymes. Hans Linser (1948) showed convincingly how isolation and correlation must play their respective parts, guided entirely by the forces immanent in the atoms.

The complicated chemical structure of organic molecules is sufficient to show us that much more complicated processes are involved than in the inorganic and inanimate sphere. The vast number of changes which take place in a corpse as a result of bacterial action is eloquent proof of the manifold opportunities of attack which a once living organism offers to catalytic influences. If we add to this the many catalysts active, in the form of enzymes and hormones, in the living organism, we get some idea of the immensely complicated processes at work. This is just what we are looking for.

If, then, we find something different in the living organism we must obviously attribute this apparent difference purely to the fact that it is more complicated; it is only this additional complexity which distinguishes animate from inanimate matter. If we can establish that the isolated phenomena are identical with those of inanimate nature, we shall be justified in regarding life as a vast complication of inorganic, i.e. physico-chemical phenomena. In this case can one speak of a difference? Is complexity a qualitative and essential difference or is it merely a quantitative one? We have shown the difference to lie in the proximity, indeed in the *accidental* proximity, of the things by which the processes are determined. Thus, as Max Hartmann (1933) said, the only difference is one of juxtaposition.

What then is an organism? An organism is no more than an excerpt from the chemical actions going on in nature. Its peculiar character consists merely in the fact that a large number of chemical processes in flux are engaged in upsetting and influencing one another. Linser (1948) called an organism "a cross-section of a plenitude of chemical processes in a state of flux".

The organism, however, is something more than a cross-section. It is something more than a juxtaposition of distinct chemical states. It is, as it were, conditioned not by the present moment, but rather by the arrangement in serried ranks of all its chemical phases. The organism is alive in so far as one phase brings about the next. We can describe a mineral or any lifeless organic compound by its properties and its chemical composition; but an organism is described by everything that occurs in it as time goes on. Inanimate matter occupying space is characterized by the spatial arrangement of its parts, but a living thing is characterized besides by the changes undergone by its constituents, by the constantly altering positions they take up. It is not possible to describe an organism purely in terms of parts existing spatially side by side; it must also be described temporally in terms of its successive states. Thus Linser spoke of *Zeitgestalt* or "time-form", which means the sum-total of all the organism's phases. Thus, besides the spatial form it shares with other material things, the organism is determined by a "time-form". Hence we cannot say that an organism is just a very complicated chemical compound. It is equally impossible to describe it as a vast sum of such compounds. From a chemical standpoint it is the sum of a large number of chemical processes.

This conclusion tells us nothing which is basically different for the "time-form", too, is simply a combination of physico-chemical processes, and the organism nothing but an assembly of the most varied chemical causal chains. Life, in other words, is movement, a vast number of movements. But the main constituents of this mobility are the forces of inorganic nature.

As all the chemical processes which we see going on are preceded by other processes, all chemical action is part of an endless chain of reaction, which can be theoretically traced back to the beginning of the world. In the organism too the chemical processes have their organic or inorganic antecedents and successors outside the organism. Linser's "time-form" in fact signifies no more than this juxtaposition of processes in the organism; the organism would appear to be nothing more than a combination of individual processes. As Linser said (1948), this assemblage of reaction chains appears to be cut off and protected from the outside world; otherwise it would have no continued existence. Linser is one of the most profound and consistent mechanists of the present day. His book shows how the forces operative in the inanimate world are correlated in the living organism. Hence his conclusion that the unique character of life is apparent rather than real. The distinction between animate and inanimate matter is one of degree, not one of kind. Linser's arguments are so plausible and convincing that it is hard to contradict them. Any refutation would have to be based on facts which are genuinely at variance with a mechanistic theory. It was clearly the plausibility of Linser's mechanistic arguments that led Hans Driesch to take up the position he did. This is all the more impressive as Driesch became the creator of the "neo-vitalism"[1] which he based on the results of his experiments in the physiology of development. Faced with the facts of morphogenesis, Driesch insisted upon the uniqueness of life. But as regards the chemistry of the subject, he took up a different standpoint. In his work *Biologische Probleme höherer Ordnung* (1941) Driesch divided the sphere of physiology into two sections, animal and vegetative. He described the division "as far more than an arbitrary division based on practical considerations. It is concerned with the innermost character of the organism." Driesch called the vegetative component the "laboratory" in contrast to the "activity-mechanism". He did not question the independent hologenous momentum of the latter, but he did not make any definite pronouncement upon the "laboratory". He wrote: "Speculations about the merogenous or hologenous structure of the processes can have only a very general and uncertain basis—a basis far more indefinite than that of morphology. It is only possible to say with justice

[1] See various papers, 1891–2; 1893a, b; 1895; 1928; 1938; 1941.

that, as regards secretion and assimilation, everything is harmoniously and purposively integrated. But this is obviously no argument for vitalism." Thus, even though the vitalist question is left open, it is clear that Driesch (1928) was aware of facts which favoured a mechanistic explanation of the life process. It must be emphasized that even such a convinced vitalist as Driesch found it impossible to decide in favour of vitalism on the grounds of metabolic and biochemical phenomena.

A mechanistic explanation seems to be supported also by the fact that the molecular character of the genes is fairly well established by the proof that they belong to the molecular order of magnitude. We know that variations in the genes have the most far-reaching consequences for the growing organism: thus what happens to the molecules has an enormous number of most complicated effects on the growth and formation of the organism. It is the intermolecular character of the genes which determines the sex of the whole organism. But if these processes go on in a single molecule, we can surely conclude that this molecule initiates a whole chain process which is no more than the mass reaction of innumerable molecules.

As a generalizing principle this explanation of life as a sum of chemical reactions is uncommonly satisfying. Life does not appear as something extraordinary, as some foreign body intruded into a mechanical world; on the contrary it takes its place in the tangible world regulated by the system of laws studied by physics. Biology, then, becomes a department of physics, just as chemistry appears to be.

The facts we have outlined can be checked at any time by experiment. They reveal life as a complex of heterogeneous chemical processes which run their course within a definite field of action, namely the living organism. Living matter is not, strictly speaking, a "being" as it possesses no single essence. More properly it consists of as many essences as it has atoms. With some degree of good will we could even say it had a merogenous individuality. It consists therefore of as many individualities as Linser's "cross-section of chemical processes" shows. What is really essential about it lies in the atomic constituents. Yet, on further consideration, this, too, seems an unsatisfactory conclusion, for the atomic constituents react with one another unceasingly in the organism only to abandon it in the end. This makes the living organism nothing but a field traversed by the various processes, and it makes no sense to look in this direction for an explanation of its nature. Of course, one can think of this field as subdivided into a number of smaller fields; with Hans Linser (1948) one can also start from the processes within the atom, the correlations of the parts which compose it, and so proceed, from the atom to the molecule and the final goal—the living organism itself. L. von Bertalanffy (1932, 1949) reasons similarly and arrives at a merogenous view of the life-principle. He thinks, too, of merogenous fields. But whereas Linser declares himself a mechanist, von Bertalanffy uses the very same arguments in support of the idea of organic integrity—wholeness. Hence it is hard to see what is "whole" in a demonstrably merogenous system. We cannot even say exactly what constitutes the living being. Is it those atoms and molecules which for the moment are flowing within it? Is it those which flowed within it a year ago? Or does it consist in those stable mineral deposits such as potassium oxalate crystals, calcareous shells or skeletal components which were and still are parts of the organism? The merogenous view of life simply does not permit of the question "who?" or "what?" When Bertalanffy talks of certain "micells" which persist and which may take up and then reject material substances, he is making an attempt to explain the "personality" or "individuality" of living matter; this attempt, however, is quite unsuccessful, for what "wholeness" could exist in such circumstances?

If we agree that Linser's argumentation confirms Bertalanffy's ideas, what we are left with is no more than "a correlation of forces in a spatially limited field" as a definition of life.

The field in this case is simply the space in which certain

laws are operative, and as such it does not interest us. We study it simply as the effect of the operative laws. Consequently we must enunciate the following principle: "Whenever the same laws are seen to operate in a similar way in different places, the spatial fields in which the laws are operative are structurally identical, for the operation of the laws is the only possible expression of a particular essential structure." The essential structure, that is to say, is identical with the laws operating in a particular spatial field. If in two different places the same physical situation occurs, the two spatial fields may be described in the same way. They are not, it is true, so alike as to exclude all individuality, but they are essentially the same, and are to be regarded as identical, inasmuch as they obey the same laws. I agree with Moritz Schlick (1925) when he said that there is no other way of describing a natural object than by the laws governing it. Nothing else can serve as a basis of comparison. If I obtain sodium reactions in two distinct places it means that sodium is present in both. If I obtain other reactions, if other laws are operative, I know I am in the presence of another element. We can now proceed from this principle to a consideration of Linser's merogenous system. If in a particular spatial field we find laws in operation which turn out to be the laws operative in numerous separate fields, we cannot regard the object as possessing a distinct nature as there are as many different natures as there are separable and distinct systems. This is not a notional abstraction, for it takes full account of the real nature of the object and its significance. As we showed to be probable in the preceding section, the living organism is therefore a complex of many isolated spatial fields.

We will now give our whole attention to the question of simple and compound substances. When chemistry was in its infancy, it was discovered that some natural substances consisted of loosely associated components which were easily separable. Thus the oxygen, nitrogen and carbon dioxide of the air are easily separated. Because air exhibits all the reactions of its constituent materials side by side, we conclude from the mass effect of the constituents that they are merely mixed. Air is said therefore to be a physical mixture. Water seems to be homogenous at first, but on analysis turns out to be compounded. Water then is a "compound". Compounds, then, are once more shown to be summations which in the mechanistic natural philosophy were tacitly assumed to be in the same category as physical mixtures. It was eventually proved that the atom itself was composite, and that all atoms consisted of a nucleus, which is universally constructed in the same way, and electrons; the differences between the elements were due entirely to differing numbers and arrangements of these uniform primary "building stones". From then on the effort to show that nature is uniform throughout knew no bounds. The ultimate explanation of all the happenings of the physical world was seen in the laws of atomic structure, whether formulated in terms of electron affinity or wave motion.

Let us examine this view as it is expressed so precisely in Moritz Schlick's philosophy of nature. Schlick distinguished between the laws of the "macrocosm" and the "microcosm". The laws of the microcosm are those which describe the processes within the atom. Schlick held that all else is a sum effect, an external expression of these microcosmic laws; it is a "bundle or collection", not of properties but of responses to laws. On the other hand, the macrocosmic laws are those which we encounter in everyday life and in the many laws of physics such as Coulomb's Law or Newton's Law of Gravitation. As Schlick (1925, p. 432) wrote:

It is evident, since nature is what we have shown it to be, that the macrocosmic laws are not the ultimate explanation; they are the consequences of hidden effects, the outward manifestations of microcosmic laws. Nature's behaviour at the macrocosmic level is absolutely determined by what goes on at the microcosmic level. If the microcosmic laws are known, it is possible to work out mathematically their effects at any finite distance. . . . Thus it is possible to deduce Coulomb's Law from the microcosmic laws expressed in Maxwell's equations.

4

Hence the macrocosmic laws, among which we include the law of entropy, are laws only in appearance. They arise, according to this theory, by a process of summation and are the external mass effect of microcosmic laws. A macrocosmic law such as that of osmotic pressure expresses no more than the total result of the, in themselves, random movements of the particles suspended in a liquid; so the effect on the macrocosmic level is solely due to the operation of mathematical probability. Hence, to use Schlick's (1925) terminology, the macrocosmic laws are those of merogenous systems. We can now make this conclusion the foundation for further theorizing.

4. INANIMATE WHOLES AND THE PRINCIPLE OF STABILITY

The ultimate phenomena of the microcosmic world are of vital importance as revealing the fundamental constituents of matter and as explaining the material processes in animate beings. Schlick (1925) himself did not suggest that the laws governing life are of a macrocosmic order. He left the problem to be clarified later by scientific specialists. But we must discuss the question whether the mechanistic definitions already given do not compel us to regard life as a macrocosmic process. If life is a correlation of molecules even these must show themselves obedient to macrocosmic laws. Even where atoms are in question we may wonder whether microcosmic or macrocosmic laws are operative. We must, therefore, go down to those laws which can be described with absolute certainty as microcosmic. These are the laws of atomic structure, the principles of matter itself.

The electron affinities which bring about a neutral state and hence a union between nucleus and electrons must be regarded as microcosmic laws. The forces responsible for the neutralization of electrical charges are the same as those which bind atoms together as molecules. This is the point, therefore, at which we must begin our attempt to explain all that happens in matter, including living matter. We are struck straight away by the remarkable sequence. Heteropolar components, nucleus and electrons, form the atom. Molecules are formed in the same way. Molecules combine together to form polymeric chains such as those of egg albumin or the polysaccharides. Finally, those microgiants, the micells, are built up from a rather indefinite number of molecules by the weak van der Waals forces. Thus one microcategory fits neatly into the next. When, we may ask, do the macrocosmic laws begin to operate and the microcosmic ones cease? We know, of course, that electrons are exchanged when homopolar or heteropolar combinations occur. The affinities of the electrons, therefore, belong without doubt to the sphere of what Schlick called microcosmic laws. To solve this difficulty we must make use of our definition of hologenous and merogenous systems.

If we hold fast to the principle that it is the laws which govern a thing which make it what it is, we shall have to find out what the relationship is between nucleus and electrons, and between them and the molecule as a whole. Does the atom, consisting as it does of nucleus and electrons, exhibit the sum of the laws governing nucleus and electrons? When the positively-charged nucleus is neutralized by the negatively-charged electrons, the quality which distinguishes the parts, namely the opposite electrical charge, disappears. The charges are integrated in the atom. In certain cases the charges are not completely extinguished. We shall have to consider this later. The fact that the nuclear charge can be completely extinguished, however, proves that electron and nucleus charges neutralize one another, and that the atom thus comes into existence. It is, of course, possible to split the atom, but while it exists, it is not the sum of the laws governing its parts; when it is broken up, it ceases to be an atom, so far as the laws governing its behaviour are concerned; what remains are the fragments, each of which behaves in conformity with its own laws. The moment an electron goes into orbit round a nucleus something new arises. Similarly, when an atom is deprived of a component, something quite new arises.

We conclude, then, that the atom is a field in which certain laws are operative, which are not the sum of as many laws as there are components. The atom, as March (1948) said, cannot be broken up into parts without ceasing to be an atom. It is, then, an entity, a whole.

Let us consider the molecule in the same way. It is quite out of the question to say that the water molecule appears to be the sum of the determinants operative in the two atoms of hydrogen and the one of oxygen. Here again there is a whole formed of parts; but, as before, the laws governing the whole are different from those operative in the parts.

The molecule can be broken up into its component atoms but it is more than the sum of its parts. In like manner starch is more than the sum of the sugar molecules from which it is built. These are clear examples of what we mean by wholes. We observe therefore two sorts of material things falling into those well-defined classes, the merogenous or the hologenous, according to the laws operative in them. The world of difference in principle between a chemical compound and a physical mixture must be borne in mind in this connection. In accordance with our terminology both atom and molecule are examples of hologenous systems.

But a hologenous whole arises in a very definite way. It is the result of regular processes and forces which are immanent in the parts from which it is built. But the parts lose their independent determinants, and in becoming members of a larger whole, alter radically. The whole, the hologenous unit, has arisen from the reacting parts. The hologeneity of an atom or a molecule is based on merogenous principle.

Mittasch's (1938) definitions are thus fully justified. To him and March (1948) we are indebted for our idea of what is meant by a "whole". But we must emphasize that such a whole depends upon the cessation of certain freedoms—in this case, the neutralization of electrical affinities.

We can make one further important statement about the atom and the molecule: Every atom and every molecule of a particular kind is in every way similar to every other atom or molecule of the same kind. Anything I can say of one iron atom applies to every iron atom in the world. If two atoms of iron can be distinguished, this is only because they are in different phases. Assuming like phases, every atom or molecule can be replaced by another of the same kind.

We want to examine now whether our description of atoms and molecules as wholes is merely arbitrary. We reached the concept of wholeness when we described the object of our investigation in terms of its characteristic dynamics. The forces whose operation we were able to express as laws were seen as determining the nature of the object. Only in so far as this is the case are we justified in calling an essential feature of the object a whole. The problem is one of causality. If an object is made up of several components and the forces governing it are not susceptible of further causal analysis we call it an entity, a whole. A composite system which, though composed of parts, cannot be analysed further in terms of cause and effect, may be described as a hologenous system. The hologenous nature of its dynamics has been proved experimentally and thus has a firm basis. What must be particularly emphasized is that we did not set out with an *a priori* concept of wholeness but came up against a definite set of facts which we designated a whole.

All the various entities owe their existence to the neutralization of opposite electrical charges; they are based, therefore, on a merogenous principle, and all have some degree of permanence. The components of the atom tend to the formation of wholes because they are by themselves impermanent and tend to neutralize one another. As independent objects, they are very unstable and therefore tend towards a more stable condition, in other words towards the hologenous union which is the atom. The atoms, too, vary in their degree of stability. Their stability varies in inverse ratio to the electrical affinities remaining unneutralized in them. Hence it is possible to draw up a table at one end of which are the extremely stable inert gases, whose atoms are incapable of further combination, and at the other end of which are the atoms whose existence as such is very ephemeral, and which form molecules with like atoms even in the elementary state. Thus oxygen in the atomic state is extremely aggressive, that is to say, unstable. Once the atoms have paired to form the molecule O_2 there is some degree of stability even if it is only slight. Metals are to some extent exceptional; they remain in the atomic state without forming molecules with their fellows. But they are prone in varying degrees to combine with atoms of a different sort. Even when the molecules have been formed, they are permanent only until they come into contact with other molecules with which they react, or show a tendency towards a mutual exchange of atoms. The tendency in all these transformations is to produce the most stable combination possible in the circumstances.

I want now to consider for a moment the causes of stability and instability. It is quite clear that these properties are not identical with the notions of molecule or atom. We have only to think of the rare gases or the halogens. Why is an inert gas so stable and a halogen atom so unstable? Why is barium sulphate so stable and nitric acid so unstable, even though both consist of molecules?

To understand this we must give a little attention to the atomic structure of the elements. We shall then recognize that the tendency of the elements towards stability is due to a microcosmic law as defined by Schlick (1925). The diagram shows a small part of the Periodic Table.

Nowadays physicists and chemists generally picture an atom as being made up of a nucleus around which a definite number of electrons revolve in a series of orbits like a miniature solar system. But each successive orbit around the nucleus, commonly called a shell, can only carry up to a certain maximum number of electrons which is different for each orbit or shell. Thus the first shell, called the K shell, can only carry a maximum of two electrons, the second one a maximum of eight electrons, and so on. Hydrogen consists of a nucleus with one electron in a single shell; helium is similar but has two electrons in the first and only shell. Again, lithium consists of a nucleus with two shells of three electrons, two in the first shell and one in the second. As the second shell, called the L shell, may

H 1
H
Hydrogen

He 2
He
Helium

Li 2,1
Li
Lithium

Be 2,2
Be
Beryllium

B 2,3
B
Boron

C 2,4
C
Carbon

N 2,5
N
Nitrogen

O 2,6
O
Oxygen

F 2,7
F
Fluorine

Ne 2,8
Ne
Neon

Na 2,8,1
Na
Sodium

Na 2,8,1
Na
atom
Sodium

F 2,7
F
atom
Fluorine

Na 2,8
Na
+ ion

F 2,8
F
− ion

Sodium fluoride

contain a maximum of eight electrons, it is essentially unsaturated, with only one in it and by addition of one electron successively to this second orbit the elements, beryllium, boron, carbon, nitrogen, oxygen, fluorine and neon are successively produced. Neon then consists of a nucleus in which the first shell has two electrons and a second shell with eight electrons. Such an element is said to be saturated and is chemically stable.

This conception of the structure of the atom may be expressed symbolically as shown in the diagram on page 41 by writing the chemical symbol for the element concerned in the centre and putting the electrons successively in order around this as a series of concentric circles of dots, or by writing down the chemical symbol for the element followed by figures for the electrons in each shell separately. Hydrogen and helium are the only elements with one orbit of electrons and these may be written as H 1 for hydrogen and He 2 for helium. The elements with two shells already listed have their first shell fully saturated and a varying number of electrons in the second and may be written as follows: lithium, Li 2, 1 (meaning two electrons in the first shell and one in the second); beryllium, Be 2, 2; boron, B 2, 3; carbon, C 2, 4; nitrogen, N 2, 5; oxygen, O 2, 6; fluorine, F 2, 7 and neon, Ne 2, 8.

We can say that the unsaturated elements are avid for electrons up to the maximum number of the shells in each case. If we look at the fluorine atom, F 2, 7, we see that the first is complete or satisfied with two electrons but the second shell has only seven electrons. It is unsaturated and given the opportunity it will satisfy its tendency to complete the second shell. Now sodium consists of a nucleus with three shells of electrons, as Na 2, 8, 1. Here the third shell, called the *M* shell, has only one electron; it is unsaturated. Thus, when an atom of sodium combines with an atom of fluorine the compound called sodium fluoride is formed, and the equation in the diagram shows that when this chemical reaction occurs the single electron from the third, or *M*, shell of sodium changes over as it were to the second, or *L*, shell of fluorine resulting in two ions of sodium fluoride. In this compound all shells are saturated and the compound is thus chemically stable. This rule, discovered by Kossel and Lewis (1946) in Bohr's atom model, is known as the "Octet Rule".

It will now be evident that the inert gases, such as neon, owe their stability to the fact that their electron spheres are saturated with electrons. All atoms with incomplete spheres, on the other hand, are unstable. They are, as it were, in search of an electron configuration like that of the inert gases. If nothing but inert gases existed, there could be no such thing as chemical change. Everything in the universe would be stable. It is clear from the above account that all unstable conditions tend towards a relatively more stable state. If I were to throw the contents of all the bottles in the laboratory into a bucket and shake them up, some very violent reactions would ensue, but in the end a stable condition would be reached, in which those compounds would be formed which were the most stable in the given circumstances.

5. FURTHER POTENTIALITIES OF INANIMATE MATTER

All that can come into existence, then, are these "wholes" and in their formation stability is always preferred to instability. At the moment it may be doubtful whether organic compounds can be formed spontaneously in nature. What is certain is that they can be manufactured. But when organic compounds are formed in this way, all that happens is that chemical valencies obtain satisfaction. However complicated the apparatus, however necessary it is to have skilled operators, nothing essentially different happens than happened when sodium fluoride or water was formed. Theoretically, at any rate, there is a continuity between all chemical compounds. It is shown in a gradual development from the simplest to the most complicated compounds, consisting of many molecules. It is scarcely possible to go on speaking of molecules when considering these gigantic structures alongside the simple molecules known to inorganic chemistry, for one can picture the latter as held together by electrons revolving in orbits common to all the atoms present. As Linser (1948) said: "In the case of the large molecules found in such compounds as the proteins, this picture can be retained only in so far as several atoms share common oscillations. But these systems of oscillation are limited to smaller groups of atoms. . . . They are linked in chains and overlap one another." I think Linser is quite right in this statement, even if I fail to see in nature the chemical process which brought this about. So gigantic a molecule is evidence of a framework, a sort of skeleton which holds all together; this framework is the carbon chain together with the reacting groups which behave as it were like organs. In the presence of enzymes, these giant molecules become extraordinarily unstable. If an entire organism, or a cell at least, is one giant molecule, we have a whole. If, on the other hand, there are many giant molecules present, all interacting continuously, we have a merogenous system, which consists of wholes but is not one itself. Since in such fluid systems all the laws governing the parts must be acting freely, there is not the smallest reason to call them wholes. Any stability possessed by such enormous molecules results from the satisfaction of primary and secondary valencies and the general tendency to pass from a less to a more stable condition. Every such molecule must be regarded as a "whole".

With Mittasch (1938) we can say that every whole is brought about by the determination of freedoms. Each whole of a lower order exhibits other freedoms which, through being in their turn determined, grow by conjunction with other wholes into wholes of a higher order. This may be expressed in another way. All "freedoms" in this sense are potentialities. Potentialities are also the electron-affinities. The element oxygen by its valency can just as easily join with hydrogen to form water as with most of the other elements to form oxides. Thus, in all the chemical constituents of matter, the basic potentiality exists which is necessary for the process of combination and the formation of higher entities.

From all this it is clear that no living organism can be a

whole in the sense described. Even if the molecules of the higher order are no longer closely-knit systems, their constituents are still bound together, however loosely, on the basis of valency. Admittedly, the number of elementary particles in a giant molecule or a micell may be inconstant, but in the living cell it is impossible any longer to find any unity based on valencies. The organism as a whole is a correlation; it is then —to use our terminology—a merogenous system.

Anything we can isolate from an organism is chemically the same as that which formerly belonged to the organism. The organism does not necessarily collapse if we remove from it whole regiments of molecules. Accordingly the most important assumption—that the organism is a closed system—is an impossible one.

If we bear in mind what has been said about molecular wholes, if we compare and relate all that we learnt from inanimate nature, we are bound to regard the animate organism as a completely merogenous system; with the aid of the theory of spatial fields we can at best show it as having a structure "merogenous" in a very high degree. In no circumstances is it possible for a living organism to be a whole in a chemical sense.

II

LAWS GOVERNING ANIMATE THINGS

1. ANIMATE AND INANIMATE SYSTEMS

(a) *General Features*

WE can now turn our attention to the forces governing life. In the inanimate sphere we have seen that whatever it is that produces a whole tends to produce the most stable compound possible in the given circumstances.

Now if life is merely a function of its material constituents, these must contain in themselves all that is necessary to give rise to living matter. The organism must be the structure which in the existing conditions is the most stable possible. In fact, however, stability is about the last attribute which one could attach to life. The life process is attended by a permanent instability.

Pflüger in 1875 tried to reproduce experimentally the circumstances of life's origin. He endeavoured to find some substance in which life was sometimes present, sometimes absent. He thought that protein was such a substance. Later, in 1915 Max Verworn, remarking on this, wrote:

> Pflüger's researches centre round the chemical properties of protein, protein being considered to be that substance with which the existence of all life is inseparably bound. According to Pflüger, there is a fundamental difference between extracted protein, such as we have in egg albumin, and protein in a living thing which builds up living substance. This difference he said, is the ability of the latter to disintegrate of itself: all living substance is in a perpetual state of dissolution; to some extent this is self-induced, but more of it is due to outside influences. Extracted protein, on the other hand, remains unchanged indefinitely under favourable conditions.

Thus Verworn and Pflüger disclosed the principle for which we are looking. Though unintentionally, they revealed the fundamental error in mechanism.

The error, quite understandable in the circumstances of the time, consisted in comparing the living being with a mineral or a salt. This comparison ran through the whole of mechanistic literature for more than a century. The result of this attitude is that a distinction was drawn between the organic and the inorganic molecule—a distinction which is not justified. The old vitalism had seen the uniqueness of life reflected in the unique and special character of the molecules of organic matter. As soon as it began to appear that the organic molecule had lost its distinctive character, mechanists began to deny the distinctive and unique character of life, too. For if organic molecules can be formed from inorganic components by means of the forces immanent in them, then (so runs the mechanistic argument) the only effective forces must be the physical forces of inorganic matter: for life is based purely upon inorganic molecules. This is how the mechanists formulate the problem and solve it. I have explained their argument in detail as forcefully and fairly as possible. But we are led to the conclusion that two problems which ought to be dealt with separately are in fact confused.

In the first place, can an organic molecule be explained on physical grounds alone? Only in this connection are we justified in comparing a mineral molecule with a molecule from a living organism. If the mechanist answers the question in the affirmative, he is already in error. In the order of inanimate matter, it is always the compound most stable in the circumstances which comes into being. Apart from such compounds as methane, the higher organic molecules are most certainly not what could be described as stable—especially when compared with simple inorganic compounds. Here we may ask if an organic compound could ever be formed in the absence of life, simply because it was the most likely outcome of the prevailing circumstances. No condition of inorganic matter is even thinkable in which carbon, oxygen and hydrogen could combine to form a sugar rather than water and carbon dioxide. The literature of the subject is rich in imaginative pictures of such situations. The earth is depicted in its early stages of development as in a hot gaseous or fluid condition. At the same time it is assumed that conditions existed which are unknown to science, and which could never be deduced from any results obtained by scientists up to date. Such pictures belong to poetry, not science. Flights of fancy are quite useless as a means of solving our present difficulties about the state of the earth in its early stages.

The laws of probability, nevertheless, enable us to get some idea of what goes on between atoms and molecules. While there are innumerable possibilities in relation to the genesis of molecular combinations, the number of probabilities is relatively very small. We need only consider compounds that are likely to come into existence. The possibility of molecules arising that have chains of atoms, and perhaps side-chains as well, is so remote that it can be left out of account. In purely natural conditions one can hardly expect such compounds to be multiplied millions of times.

The organic molecules are not the most stable, nor are they synthesized in such a way as to make it probable that they would develop from purely inorganic matter in any conditions known to physical science. Thus, even on the molecular level, there must be specific starting points for the formation of organic compounds, and these are not apparent outside the sphere of life. This being so, the premisses on which the mechanistic theory is based are destroyed. But this is a purely chemical question and the real centre of the problem remains untouched.

In respect to the nature and origins of life, is the appearance of life essentially bound up with the presence of molecules of a certain definite form and character? The answer is, of course, "Yes". Life cannot appear unless molecules of a special constitution are available. Is life then the automatic consequence of the presence and juxtaposition of the necessary components? The answer here is a definite "No". Molecules that are identical can be the components as easily of a dead as of a living organism. The molecules which are necessary to life can come into being only in the "unnatural" conditions to which the name "life" is given. They are the product and consequence of life; they do not themselves give rise to life.

The opposite of "living" is not "inorganic", but "dead". The living organism is not to be contrasted with a mineral but with a corpse. We cannot say molecules are alive; they may be regarded more appropriately as the stage upon which the drama of life is enacted. In another sense, of course, the process which we call life can be compared with the phenomena of inanimate nature. In what sense are life-phenomena unique, and do they correspond in any points, important or unimportant, with the phenomena of inanimate nature? Our problem is now to decide upon these matters.

(b) *Life as a Source of Energy*

The simple means of determining whether a human being or one of the higher animals is alive or dead is by observing the presence or absence of breathing. But breathing is simply the outward sign of a much more important criterion of life, namely metabolism. Does this process of change imply anything other than decay? By breathing, a living organism destroys its own store of material. Free oxygen, the "life element", combines with the carbon atoms stored in the complex organic molecule to form the simple carbon dioxide. This involves tearing their chain-like framework out of the molecules and separating the links from one another. The molecule breaks up into its constituents, which then have to be expelled from the body. The life-process thus appears as the oxidation of the living tissues by free oxygen. This at any rate applies to the great majority of living creatures which are therefore classified as "aerobic". The so-called "anaerobic" organisms can live in an environment having little or no oxygen. Weinland's researches on intestinal worms have shown

that in these creatures glycogen is changed into valerianic acid
and carbon dioxide. Weinland describes this process as fermentation. In alcoholic fermentation the various yeasts break
up sugar anaerobically into ethyl alcohol and carbon dioxide.
Furthermore, *Clostridium Pasteurianum*, a bacterium, discovered by Winogradsky, which can fix atmospheric nitrogen,
also breaks up sugar anaerobically without using free oxygen.
In both intestinal worms and other intestinal parasites large
quantities of glycogen or paraglycogen are stored and broken
up again by them as by other creatures. This is sufficient to
show that the oxidation of living matter by free oxygen is not
universal and does not occur in all creatures showing signs of
life. Does this mean that respiration in the form of oxidation
is not an essential vital phenomenon? Another important
aspect of respiration must be considered before we can answer
this question.

In normal sugar respiration the process is not initiated by
the meeting of sugar molecules with free oxygen. In the absence
of air and with the aid of special enzymes known as oxidases,
the oxygen in the molecule is "loosened" and taken up by
another molecule. In a similar manner, other enzymes known
as dehydrases detach hydrogen from one molecule and incorporate it into another. In these cases different molecules
interact, the donor giving to the recipient either an oxygen or
a hydrogen atom. Free oxygen comes into the process only
when each carbon atom in the molecule is oxidized to carbon
dioxide, and each hydrogen atom is oxidized to water. I
think we can assume then that in the respiration of the
higher animals and plants an anaerobic process precedes the
final oxidation by free oxygen. The process of respiration in
anaerobic organisms appears, then, to be part of the process
of respiration observable in aerobic organisms. It is a form
specially adapted to their peculiar conditions of life. Thus
respiration is far from being a simple process. One finds in
addition individual variations and special simplifications of
the process. Thus plants which are normally aerobic generate
carbon dioxide in the absence of oxygen, a proof that carbon

can be oxidized without oxygen from outside. It is obvious that in this case just one act of a two-act drama is performed.

From the foregoing it appears that respiration covers a considerable number of processes which appear in complex and simple forms. The object of all of them, however, is the same: the liberation of energy for the service of the subject.

Everything occurring in the world of matter, including life, may be described as transformation of energy. Energy in the widest sense may be described as either actual work or potential work. Accordingly, we can speak of actual energy and potential energy, i.e. energy at the moment latent, but capable of becoming operative in appropriate circumstances. If from this angle we consider chemical combinations and double decompositions through which one compound arises from another, two empirical possibilities arise. When a compound is formed, energy is either liberated (as in the case of water) or absorbed. In the first case the compound contains no potential energy; on the contrary the same amount of energy which is needed for the separation of the compound into its elements is dissipated when they combine. Such a combination is said to be "exothermic". If, on the other hand, energy is absorbed when a combination occurs, this energy is given up when the compound is split up. Such a combination is said to be "endothermic".

All the chemical combinations concerned in metabolism in the living organism are endothermic. In order, therefore, to be able to give out energy in vital activity, energy must be absorbed and stored in the organism as potential energy until set free again as required. Respiration is the process by which potential energy is transformed into actual energy to be used in vital processes. However, as we have seen, the mechanical process of carbohydrate oxidation is not the same in all living creatures. Yet in both aerobic and anaerobic respiration a material change occurs which is accompanied by a rise in temperature. Potential energy is continuously transformed into actual energy. The energy in the material available at the

5

beginning is reduced stage by stage until in the end all that is left is ammonia, carbon dioxide and water.

We see, therefore, a completely harmonious series of separate physico-chemical processes all leading to the same end. Each process seen by itself is in no way unique; it may be simulated in a test-tube. The end result of all the processes combined together, however, is that energy is made available to initiate other processes in the organism.

Also striking is the fact that so long as the compounds are charged with energy they can be regarded as parts of the body. But as soon as the store of energy has been exhausted as a result of many successive changes, the materials cease to be parts of the body; they become the end or waste products. By a further series of physico-chemical processes they are then eliminated from the body. What sort of materials are these that are changed by respiration and finally eliminated?

In former times, in the days of classical mechanism, it was assumed that the "living" protein molecule, or a complex of proteins—Verworn's "biogen",[1] Altmann's "granulum"[2] or Nägeli's "micell"[3]—decomposed as a result of its immanent structure, and disintegrated into its constituents. It was thought that protein was the only vital material that needed to be considered, for animals find protein absolutely necessary for their nutrition, and excrete a compound containing nitrogen— ammonia, urea or uric acid. It is true that plants, with their greater versatility in the synthesis of compounds, do not require protein in their food; but they do need nitrogen, with which they can synthesize protein for themselves. This nitrogen may come in the form of nitrates or as atmospheric nitrogen. Life was thought to be the result of the physical interaction of the protein molecules.

Today it is becoming clearer and clearer that the process of metabolism is bound up more particularly, not with the proteins, but with the carbohydrates and, in particular, glucose; it is the combustion of these substances which produces energy.

---

[1] 1915.   [2] 1890–4.   [3] 1862.

Can we then apply what the classical mechanists said of proteins to the carbohydrates? Certainly not. Carbohydrates are oxidized not only to produce energy for vital activity but also to provide that energy which is stored in the protein and fat compounds. In the animal organism both protein and sugar are constantly being decomposed; for in animal catabolism carbon dioxide and water are not the only end-products; we also regularly find urea and uric acid as waste products— nitrogen compounds which are clearly derived from proteins. By his experimental oxidation of the amino-acid cystine suspended on blood charcoal, Warburg[4] was able to demonstrate that his end-products were exactly those produced in the living cell—ammonia, carbon dioxide and sulphuric acid. Thus there is no doubt that protein is being constantly decomposed during energy production in the animal organism. But the fungus *Aspergillus niger* grows well when supplied with peptones and amino-acids. On the other hand, in the higher plants it is impossible to speak with regularity of a respiration involving proteins. Nevertheless, under adverse conditions even a plant is capable of degrading protein. The economical and versatile plant does not simply excrete the final waste product ammonia, but further changes and renders it useful once more. As plants do not excrete nitrogenous waste matter—the proof of protein decomposition—it is perhaps impossible to give here an absolute verdict. Fats, too, are decomposed to supply energy.

Whatever is decomposed and lost in respiration involves in every case a breakdown of materials which once formed parts of a living body. According to modern mechanistic views, this breakdown is due to the purely fortuitous circumstance that the energy-storing molecules chance to meet with the specific enzymes and then accidentally make contact with oxygen; as a result of these meetings the molecule happens by chance to break down. The causes are thus seen to lie exclusively in the energy-storing molecules, the enzymes and free oxygen. Apart from the accumulation of chance happenings, which verges on

[4] 1921, 1928, 1932.

the miraculous,[5] no objection can be raised to the facts as stated. I want now to mention one more fact which is so obvious that it amounts to a truism.

Many organisms deposit fat in certain tissues and, given an adequate diet, this fat is not normally used. But if the sources of energy in the body are insufficient either owing to lack of nourishment or because excessive demands are made upon them, the stored fat is metabolized and the potential energy stored in it is used to make up for the lack of carbohydrates. Furthermore, an organism which is hungry continues to excrete urine, and this means that it is consuming protein. I have already mentioned that protein metabolism occurs also in plants whose normal respiration depends upon the metabolism of carbohydrates. One source of energy can, therefore, replace the other when necessary to the organism; and if, in practice, several metabolic processes are at work together, the separate sources of energy are indistinguishable as regards the work they do. I shall have more to say about this important circumstance and its consequences. For the moment let us summarize our conclusions: All life consists in the production of energy, due to the endothermic character of living organisms. All processes of this kind are a constant, never-broken chain of reactions accompanied by a rise in temperature. The living substance lives by a process of degradation of complex chemical compounds.

(c) *Growth and Decay*

If a living system is to persist and not disintegrate with the loss of all its energy, it must replace its losses with something structurally equivalent. The loss due to the expenditure of energy must be succeeded by growth in which energy is stored. The two processes are continuous so that a state of "fluid equilibrium" is achieved. The term "equilibrium", however, is not always quite applicable. When a living organism is growing, building exceeds demolition, so that the total amount of

---

[5] I think that few biochemists would express the matter in this way.—Editor.

substance is increased. The process can go on also in reverse, as in perennial plants, where a large part of the organism may be lost. Here there is a partial collapse of the organism with no corresponding reconstruction. Besides this, cellulose in plants, calcareous shells and horny layers in vertebrates are built up and remain present during the life of the organism. Here development of new structures is opposed by attrition, wear— not breakdown.

In order to obtain energy, materials must be broken down chemically; growth on the other hand demands chemical synthesis. Green plants are able to carry out this basic and essential process of energy-storing; non-green plants, and all animals, enter into the process at a certain point by feeding upon materials in which energy has been chemically stored by the others. Most of the energy expended in vital activity is derived from sunlight via the green plants. With very little qualification, one could say that life is transformed sunlight. The first energy-charged substance to be produced in the plant is carbohydrate, in the available form of sugar or the unavailable form of starch. All the other chemical compounds produced in the plant are ultimately derivatives of sugar.

In normal respiration organic compounds are oxidized by free oxygen, and energy is thereby released. The same result can be obtained in another way by anaerobic organisms. There are different methods of storing energy corresponding to these different ways of releasing it. The sun is the source of energy for most organisms; it is made use of by the process known as photosynthesis. Nevertheless there are a few lower organisms which can assimilate carbon dioxide even in the dark. The energy required for this is obtained by chemical reactions. These autotrophic organisms store energy by chemosynthesis instead of photosynthesis. The sulphur bacteria, for example, oxidize sulphuretted hydrogen to sulphur or sulphuric acid; the nitrifying bacteria oxidize ammonia to nitrites, and other bacteria oxidize these further to nitrates. In the same way, and with the same purpose, iron bacteria transform ferrous oxide into ferric oxide; and hydrogen bacteria use hydrogen to form water. In every case energy is produced which has the same function as solar energy; and in every case energy is captured and stored.

2. THE PRINCIPLE OF INSTABILITY

Life, as we have seen, is a continual ebb and flow. While in the sphere of inanimate matter the tendency is always towards a state of stability, the opposite is the case with animate things. The substances active in a living body are in constant movement and only reach a state of rest on being ejected. If one of the chemical processes associated with life is isolated and simulated in a test-tube, all that is observable is what is characteristic of chemical reactions. The end result is always a state of stability and inaction. The sum-total of these processes in the living organism, however, all acting in harmony, is a situation quite foreign to the sphere of inanimate matter.

When a body reaches a state in which all its processes tend to a state of stability it is dying. A corpse is a conglomeration of numerous organic molecules; its molecular structure and the relation of its parts witness to a principle of order once operative within it. As this principle is no longer at work, the molecules go their own ways, the ways of inanimate molecules, and end in a merogenous type of stability. In living matter, therefore, a principle of order reigns which causes the individual parts to move on lines different to those they would follow if left to themselves. The corpse lacks this principle of order. Life, then is essentially this principle of order. Now the order which governs the relationship of the parts of a living organism is fundamentally different from that applicable to anything else. We must, therefore, assume, as the principle of this order, a factor quite distinct from any of the purely structural relationships of the separate material components of the organism. It is incredible that a complex of substances, all tending towards a state of stability, would produce the permanent chemical instability which is characteristic of animate matter.

3. WHAT IS LIVING IN THE ORGANISM?

The older mechanistic theory regarded the protein molecules as the only seats of life. The newer mechanistic theory, on the other hand, regards the whole integrated organism as the living unit. Life, then, is the sum of the effects of a number of molecular processes. Our enquiries up to now have led us to one definite conclusion: that the living organism exhibits chemical processes which tend in a direction of which the molecules by themselves are quite incapable. How could this apparently self-evident fact be so deliberately ignored? Mechanists had, of course, to find a way out and had recourse to a *deus ex machina*. It is interesting here to compare the classical mechanistic theory, as it was at the turn of the century, with the mechanistic theory of today. If an organism is divided up into areas, a compound taken from one of these areas can be made to react in isolation exactly as it reacts in the living organism. Thus one can mix pepsin and hydrochloric acid in a test-tube, and by this mixture protein can be digested. This is exactly the process which goes on in the stomachs of vertebrates. The partially-digested matter can then be further digested with trypsin, as happens in the duodenum. The digestion can be completed with erepsin. Similar experiments can be carried out with liver extracts and blood plasma. The conclusion is drawn from this that, as these separate processes occur in the test-tube exactly as they do in an organism, life is no more than the sum of these processes in a certain combination. Any difficulties which were certainly felt, if seldom expressed, were disposed of in various ways.

The classical mechanists found it difficult to picture such an extensive correlation in the operations of the individual molecules. Not without some justification they saw life exclusively as a function of the cell. Schwann and Schleiden[6] both thought of the cell as the physical unit of life. Life was regarded as the physical function of certain quite peculiar departments, rather like a very complicated catalyst; life was the remarkable

[6] 1839 and 1833.

physical activity of this "catalyst". In this way life's driving power was thought to be a corporeal entity. By a physico-chemical structure, yet to be discovered, this entity was so able to influence the other materials that they all contributed their shares to the process. Life, thought these theorists, had certain distinct centres which would have to be discovered. One point was clear: these centres were in some way connected with the cell and its functions. As the cell itself cannot be this vital particle, and as it cannot be looked for outside the cell, the cell must at least contain it. Life is metabolism; life must, therefore, be thought of as something constant, like a chemical radical, which rejects certain materials, attracts others, and then rejects these once more. As the fundamental thing in life is always protein, the elementary particle we are looking for must be a protein radical. This was the view which led to the idea of a living protein molecule. The non-proteins in the cell were in this case derivatives, reserve materials or waste products of these primary vital particles. Apart from these tiny entities, everything else appeared to be more or less inanimate.

These ideas of the older mechanists persist even today, though in somewhat different dress. Some people expect us to see the genes as the "elements of life". In that case we shall have to transfer our expectations of the "biogens" to the genes. It appears from recent cytological literature that the new aspirant to the position of life's micro-element is the lipoid. Anything then which does not fit into these chosen biological fields—fibres of connective tissue or nerve fibres, for example —has to be relegated to the position of one of their mechanical by-products. The lamellae of the bones (with the exception of the osteoblasts), cellulose, cuticles, cell sap and horny excrescences are certainly of this nature.

In the light of this theory it is not a little astonishing to discover that the fibres of connective tissue are capable of independent growth and subdivision. Facts of this sort led people like Schaffer (1933) and Huzella (1941) to the conclusion that there are living things in the organism even outside the cells. Although structures of this kind originate in cells, they do not remain dependent upon the cell for their continued life. This should be kept in mind whenever there is any question of designating micells or genes as the elements of life.

When these views were making headway, it was known that, especially in plants, it is sugar, and particularly the simple glucose, no complex biogen, which by its complete breakdown yields the energy necessary for living processes, the energy which is sometimes identified with life. It is true that this breakdown is regulated, but the regulating agents are nothing other than molecular catalysts, enzymes, vitamins and hormones; all that we call metabolism is brought about by their activity. Even if the undoubtedly dead tissues, such as cuticles or bones (excluding the osteoblasts), have no living functions, their existence has an effect upon the metabolic process. This may be seen in the regulative phenomena of injuries, skin casting, etc. Thus even that which is "dead" in the organism affects the general organization of the life within it, just as, in the reverse direction, the living structure gives rise to and fixes the character of what is dead. Today, then, it is impossible to say where living tissue ends and waste-product begins. This view guided the thought of Hans Linser (1948), who must be regarded as the most thoroughgoing representative of the newer mechanistic theory. According to him there are molecules everywhere. The processes which go on in these molecules are alike in living and lifeless matter. But owing to the fact that some of these molecules are highly complex, through the operation of the van der Waals forces, other molecules of a similar constitution are brought into existence. Combining with the original molecules, these form a whole superior to them both separately. Reaction and interaction go on continuously, producing the phenomenon we call life. On this view it is idle to try to distinguish between what is more and what is less alive: life consists exclusively in a correlation between all these parts and particles. We cannot say this and that lives; everything shows signs of life. These contrasted forms of mechanism may be summarized as follows:

1. In the older mechanism, life is a physico-chemical process

which goes on in certain conglomerations of molecules; this process sets off a number of peculiar activities loosely related to it. The vital process, therefore, has its centres.

2. In the newer mechanism, nothing can be said to be alive in itself. Processes, in themselves devoid of life, produce, by a process of summation, the phenomenon we call "life". Bertalanffy (1949) takes up a position between these two views.

There is no doubt that the newer mechanist is right in saying that life consists in a combined functioning of all the parts. Nevertheless we cannot quite escape from the position of the older mechanists, because in this combined action of the various parts, some have a more fundamental and primary rôle than others. For example, a living cell is somehow more alive than the wood fibre formed from it. There is a hierarchical order in the life processes. If we regard the aragonite shell of a snail as lifeless and its protoplasm as alive, where is the dividing line? If it were possible to say which part of an organism is alive or dead, we might be able to say to what extent a molecule participates in the life process. In the case of the snail's shell this is relatively easy to decide. The shell itself is dead but the epithelial cells of the mantle are alive. But let us consider for a moment a digestive enzyme. This would appear to be something separated from the body and therefore lifeless, like the snail's shell. But is life conceivable without digestive enzymes? Whenever anything takes a high place in the hierarchy of life's order, it is invariably a nucleoprotein, the material of which genes consist. Nucleoproteins operate primarily as catalysts, but so do enzymes. Where then is the dividing line? The newer mechanist seems to be right in saying that the molecules even of the key protein compounds are indistinguishable structurally from inanimate matter, except as regards their origin. Protein molecules, then, are in a sense mechanical structures; in the order of being, they are on the same level as other inanimate substances; yet they cannot come into existence entirely by means of the causes operating in lifeless matter. The mechanist is therefore wrong in affirming that organic molecules develop in inanimate matter. It is true, however, that the molecules connected with life are marked off by no clear boundary line from those of inorganic matter. When the mechanist goes on to affirm that a living organism is the sum of millions of inanimate factors, he is again wrong, but this time because he overlooks an essential feature of life.

All molecules result from an electro-chemical tendency to neutralization. They are therefore expressions of tendencies towards stability. But is it possible for millions of such tendencies to stability to add up to a tendency towards instability? We can only accept this if we invoke Bertalanffy's (1949) "fluid equilibrium" as the *deus ex machina*. Thus this "fluid equilibrium" of the present-day mechanists plays the same mysterious rôle as the "protein conglomerate" used to do. Hence, if we descend to the level of micro-chemistry, we can say of nothing that it is alive as such; still less can we say that it is more alive than something else. The tendency to instability is not natural to the molecules; it must be produced by a factor which is not identical with the molecules themselves nor with the forces residing in them.

Is it possible to regard this "instability factor" as something material, as a sort of catalyst or microscopic granule? We have already excluded this possibility. We saw that it was one of the errors of the earlier mechanists. If we did so regard it, we should first have to assume the existence of laws in the molecular sphere which run completely counter to all that physics has up to now been able to tell us of those applicable to molecules. Hence the term "molecule" would be completely out of place. Secondly, every molecular structure, every spatial field of operation, is localized in a particular spot; it must be near enough to the materials upon which it has an effect, and must be more remote from other materials. We should, then, be able to point to a particular spot in which these effective molecular factors are localized. But the factor we are looking for affects the most diverse molecules and enters into the most varied processes. It cannot, therefore, be anything comparable to what we normally call a "body". An organism is composed exclusively of molecules; the material of which it is made consists of nothing else. This instability factor therefore must be sought elsewhere than in the domain of matter.

This leads inevitably to a further question. In the last resort, does this instability factor live somehow apart? Is it alone alive while everything material is dead? It is impossible to affirm this either. The independence of the instability factor can be proved scientifically only if it can be isolated in some way or other. Life, however, is a phenomenon enacted in material substances. We are familiar with inanimate matter, but all we know of this instability factor is that it makes matter live. Material substances are at one time alive, at another lifeless. We find in living beings the same molecules as we find in corpses, the same molecules as we analyse in the test-tube; hence the instability factor is a sphere of activity into which materials enter, and which they later leave. Life is enacted in a "field", a field which we know is not empty of material substances; yet life is recognizably present because the materials which compose it are subject to laws while within it which are different from those they obey when outside it. Life is the name we give to those phenomena which material substances, in themselves lifeless, exhibit when subject to the influence of the immaterial instability factor. Every field filled with matter and under the control of the instability factor is alive.

4. ORDER

A molecule represents a definite order which is expressed in the laws that govern it. In this sense a definite order reigns also among the laws governing the combinations of atoms and molecules. When two molecules combine, the way in which they do so is determined by their structure. The order in which chemical changes occur is therefore determined by the order which determines the reacting molecules. From the character of the reacting molecules or atoms it is possible to infer what compounds will arise.

In the sphere of inanimate nature we can go further; we can infer backwards to the starting point. From the presence of common salt we can infer the pre-existence of sodium and chlorine ions which must have interacted. From the nature of the compound NaCl we can thus infer how Na and Cl have acted. If we now apply this method to the sphere of animate matter, we find that this contact is completely lacking. From the chemical premises it is not possible either to infer the effect upon animate matter, or to infer from the effects in animate matter the chemical premises. The chemical factors here result in an instability which cannot be deduced from tendencies whose direction is wholly towards stability. To the molecular data with which we are familiar we are obliged therefore to assume another factor, the one which produces this instability. Where are we to find the chain of causality which underlies life? How is it ordered and to what end?

The first relevant principle of order is that of the initial organization. If a living process is to run its course, a certain organization must come first. The organism must exist. A whole mass of molecules of very special construction must be present. Such molecules cannot possibly have come into existence in lifeless nature. The second principle of order operates once the necessary initial order is present. It is the principle which causes the separate processes to work in harmony. I shall call it the law of succession. It is a perfectly simple chemical reaction which is illustrated in animal nutrition. Here all compounds of high molecular weight, such as proteins, fats and polysaccharides, are broken up into simple amino-acids, fatty acids, glycerine and monosaccharides. This decomposition may take place in a series of separate stages as in the breakdown of protein by pepsin, trypsin and erepsin. The operative enzymes are hydrolases, and each is appropriate for a particular process and each is produced by distinctive processes. All these processes are integrated; the enzymes fit into the molecules, like keys in locks, and open them up. In nutrition energy is not set free by this complex process; the hydrolases do not attack the solid framework of the molecule, but the result is that the foodstuffs are robbed of their peculiarities and split up into unspecific "building bricks". But these units are once more built up by hydrolases (still without

loss of energy) into substances suitable for body-building. Only
at this point do the desmolases—completely different enzymes
—go into action and penetrate deep into the molecular structure; they, assisted later by free oxygen, break the molecules
up into simple fragments. Only at this stage is stored energy set
free. In isolation each chemical process is a simple one; taken
all together they reveal a purposive co-ordination which in the
inorganic world would be the height of improbability. We see
the building of chemical houses of cards—unstable equilibria
built and then demolished by desmolases and oxygen. "Im-
possibly" complicated substances are formed through a purposive concatenation of reactions, and these substances are
repeatedly brought into situations in which they can have no
permanent existence. It is this "refined" principle of order
which raises and then demolishes living structures. No compound produced purely by chance could raise so complicated
and unstable a structure; it is just as unlikely that the very
same system should accidentally and at the same time bring
about its demolition. This order, so uncharacteristic of molecules, must lie outside the order of the molecules involved, and
it must be purposive. It must be meaningful too because the
separate reactions can be understood only in the light of the
function they subserve as links in the chain. The chain can be
understood only in the light of the result of the separate processes. That the order is purposive is clear from the fact that
the beginning and end of the chain are related in a way which
is quite different from a purely chemical relationship.

Most mechanists believe that it was a series of chance events
which generated these gigantic molecules and then made them
incapable of maintaining themselves so that they broke up
while releasing energy. According to them, the direction was
given at the start by the "unnatural" molecules themselves.
The only unnatural thing about these molecules, of course, is
the theory which would make them products of the inorganic
world. Ignoring this for the moment, however, and admitting
the existence of the molecules, the intolerance of enzymes towards these molecular monsters would soon set off an irre-

versible process which would even out all tensions and culminate in a state of stability, that is to say, death. The fact, however, that the whole process is repeated over and over again, as in perpetual motion, is an indication that it is under the control of a principle which organizes the separate reactions in a series, and prevents the ever-moving process from ever coming to rest or reaching a state of stability. This could happen only if the primary atomic order were subjected to a principle of order which is opposed to the primary order of the electro-affinities.

The series of reactions do not proceed only side by side; they proceed also concentrically. For example, one series of reactions at a certain stage produces an enzyme which at one point is introduced into another series of reactions by which bodily substance is being built up or broken down. Decomposition products from a series of reactions are separated and go their different ways under the influence of specific enzymes. Thus here, too, another law of order is at work, and this cannot be distinguished in any objective way from those already mentioned. It reveals yet another aspect of the general or total organization. We shall call this the law of "coaction". The effects as a whole serve the end to which they are directed. Only if a particular effect is required do the many series of reactions occur. In this case, however, the various reaction series assist and complete one another.

As already stated, energy may be generated from carbohydrates, fats or proteins. If the organism is short of food materials, proteins may be used as a substitute. This amazing fact cannot be explained by the mechanistic theory, for mechanistically anabolism would have to be pictured as follows: The presence of sugar, fat and proteins together with a series of desmolases and oxygen would have to be assumed. These raw materials would then have to react together in such a way that energy resulted. The energy produced in this case would have to depend upon the quantities of the reacting materials. But when there is no sugar, protein and fat take its place as generators of energy. Sugar, fat and protein are completely different compounds; hence the processes which bring about their oxidation are just as different. *These series of reactions are in fact quite independent but in case of need they can supplement one another and can even replace one another.*

As in respiration quite distinct substances are consumed by quite different processes, it cannot be true that a correlation of the compounds involved is responsible for the generation of energy. Even assuming that the presence of carbohydrate operates as an anti-enzyme and prevents the decomposition of protein, it remains a fact that, from the point of view of the effect, it does not matter which of these materials produces the energy. The process is not the inevitable result of the means present; it is the end result which determines the process. Energy cannot be produced without the necessary raw materials. There must be molecules which store up energy or there would be nothing on which to build. Once the materials are there energy must be produced. The process by which energy is liberated can vary; it is the end which sets the process in movement. Thus in a living organism it is not possible to see at first from the effect from what source the energy is derived. Since, then, different chains of reactions follow from different initial materials, the molecules of these materials cannot be the exclusive determinants of the effect, for it is the effect which sets the process going; the goal is the cause of the process. It is not true then that *materia producit effectum.* What is true is that *e materia effectus producitur.* In other words, the factor of order cannot be identical with the material which yields the energy, since it produces the same result from the most varied materials. A more typical case than this of what we mean by a "final cause" could not be imagined. The purpose or goal is that which originates the whole process.

5. BIODYNAMIC WHOLENESS

Early in this book the opposition between the views of Democritus and Aristotle was mentioned. The mechanistic theory of today, with one important variation, follows Democritus, while vitalism may be regarded as a continuation of Aristotle's teaching. Although, at first sight, these thinkers appear to be opposed, the knowledge we have today enables us to see that both were justified.

The atoms of Democritus, whether interpreted as corpuscular or as waves, are the basic particles of matter. In the form of electrical charges, they determine its potentialities. Merogenous systems—even in lifeless matter—are built up by correlations of these particles acting in accordance with rigid laws. Now, if there is no *materia prima*, and if a *materia signata* has existed from the beginning in the form of atoms and molecules, we must grant that some immaterial factor attacks these particles, these "granules", binds them into a whole, and gives them a stamp which the variant parts could never give. This fact is not stated as a result of knowledge derived from outside the sphere of science. Our starting point was matter itself, matter which can be weighed and measured, matter whose changes can be observed and compared; not for one moment has this matter been left out of account. We did not find ourselves compelled like Rickert (1921) to change our viewpoint when we looked upon living beings not as atoms and molecules, but as organisms. We did not observe the living being as such; we observed the atoms and molecules which compose it, and saw that these were the same elementary particles as those which occur in inanimate matter. We were, nevertheless, led to the definite conclusion that the granules, with their electro-affinities, form structures which could never arise as a result of inanimate action. We further discovered, on observing the same materials chemically, that they were subject to laws quite different from those immanent in the particles. We followed the path of the mechanists and we fully admit the rights of their claim, but in pursuing it without prejudice to the end, we reached the position of the vitalists. We had to discard the so-called "wholeness" theory, for in it incommensurable ideas yield an imaginary but not objective whole. The mechanistic theory, on the other hand, deserves to be taken seriously; it is based on solid thought and experiment which must not be suddenly checked by a prejudice. Concentration on the idea of wholeness must, in consequence, lead to subjectivism and

6

finally to agnosticism, while mechanism, carried to its logical conclusion, must end in vitalism. We endeavoured to prove this in the sphere of biochemistry, which most of the vitalists have surrendered to the mechanists.

If then we accept in all sincerity the truths of chemistry and the law of the conservation of energy and of matter, we must see life as a special form of causality. I claim that this form of causality has a real existence independent of that applying to inanimate matter. In this sense the organism has been treated as a system of chemical and dynamic relationships, and the laws operating in it have been examined.

These laws have been found to be different from those we see operating in inanimate matter. Among the separate chemical processes there exists a purposive order which is revealed as an instability in the activities of the molecules.

But, opposed to this instability of the molecular constituents, a stability makes its appearance—the stability of the living organism. It is here that the antagonism of the two principles is clearly revealed. The animate thing, as such, maintains itself in a state of stability, while the substances which compose it appear unstable. As soon as the living organism ceases to live and so loses its stability as a living being, the molecules go their own merogenous ways and become stable themselves. Any tendency to stability in the sphere of the chemical constituents is an interference with the course of life, or a symptom of disease, and leads, as it gains ground, to death. This antagonism between the two principles is itself enough to prove the distinctness of animate matter.

We have shown that it is the final purpose which initiates the life processes. We must now ask what the purpose is to which all the unstable living processes are directed. We saw that a great many chemical reactions are arranged in series in a very exceptional way. We called this the "law of succession" —the law governing the succession of one thing to another. We saw, too, that the successive series are so arranged that they can compete and even take the place of another. The various laws appear, therefore, to express an ordering principle to which the organism is subject; and subjection to law is a concept which we ascribe to the order we recognize in things. Now, in a wider sense, we can describe anything as a whole which is made such by a principle of order. It is whole because a unity arises from the parts. But, as I have explained, the parts in an organism in no circumstances form a whole by themselves. They are made whole only by the order which connects their varying phenomena. This order is a principle which does not rest upon the effect of the various parts (as in the case of molecules). It must itself contain "wholeness" as its determining characteristic, for it produces wholeness where wholeness would not otherwise exist. Thus we know the effect: but who or what produces it?

The answer of the mechanists is, "The several laws governing the single molecules." Since they concentrate their attention entirely upon these, they cannot accept the idea of wholeness in our sense, and insist that the effect is manifold. But we have now shown the effect to be a whole. Now if we examine life in its chemo-dynamic aspects we shall inevitably reach a valuable viewpoint. The factor of wholeness is often pictured as a sort of model, a rigid immaterial form, or as a seal impressed upon the sealing wax of matter. But looked at chemo-dynamically, life is seen, not as the outward expression of something fixed and already "given", but as something happening, something flowing on, something dynamic. Our examination of the molecules revealed them as caught up, as it were, in the stream of something happening, a stream which must be viewed as a whole. The potentialities of the individual constituents are not in the least altered; they are, however, set in a definite direction so that all their changes contribute to produce a single dynamic living form. This dynamic wholeness factor may be usefully described as a field of operation. This field of operation makes use of the chemical potentialities by causing them to realize a purpose. We cannot say, therefore, that the separate chemical components, in entering the life process, are robbed of their original potentialities. What really happens may be best described as a *superpositio*. Molecules and atoms are present in full force with all their capabilities.

In speaking of merogenously formed wholes, we established that they are produced solely by the neutralization of electro-affinities. Thus when hydrogen and oxygen combine to form water the previously free affinities are lost. The two hydrogen atoms and the oxygen atom are no longer present in the water molecule, for they are neutralized; therefore they are changed. If, on the other hand, the atoms are separated again, the newly-formed hydrogen and oxygen atoms are no longer what they were in the water molecule, for they are now subject to different laws. The laws governing anything which exists are the criterion of its nature. If these change, the thing itself changes, too. Hence March (1948) was quite right in affirming that neither atoms nor molecules permit of further analysis on a causal basis.

Now the atoms and molecules of living matter are the same as they would have been if they had not formed part of a living organism. If any free valencies exist, they have not been determined by the association of giant molecules in forming an organism. What does happen is that the constituents of the various parts of the organism are being freshly grouped all the time to form new wholes; this finds its expression in the instability of life. The wholeness of life is recognizable only in the manner in which these changes are controlled, and the essential criterion of the controls is their purposiveness. Hence, in the chemo-dynamic sphere, it is not correct to say that wholeness causes purposiveness. Rather is it purposiveness which constitutes wholeness.

Our examination of the living organism has led us to the conclusion that the goal aimed at by separate chemical processes is also the cause of those processes. Because there is a correspondence between aim and cause, we conclude that wholeness is both aim and cause. We can now say that a principle of wholeness is the cause of the chemo-dynamic laws of life.

To sum up—the wholeness factor in the chemo-dynamic sphere is a hologenous principle. What it produces is a totality, a hologenous system. The living organism is an event in the chemo-dynamic world; it is a hologenous system built upon a hologenous principle. The characteristic of both system and principle is the ordering of the separate chemical processes towards a definite end.

III

THE LIVING FORM

1. THE PROBLEM OF MORPHOGENESIS

THE real battlefield of biological theory in most people's
eyes is the problem of form. Modern vitalism originated
in research into the origin of the living form. In previous
chapters we had to break new ground to arrive at some knowledge based on experiment but we now find ourselves upon a
well-trodden path. There is such a mass of literary material at
our disposal that no one man could hope to cope with it all.
To show what the form problem is, I intend, therefore, to
summarize the most important theories as briefly as possible.
My idea is simply to show where the true problem lies and
what solutions are possible.

The two basic theories are associated with the names of
Weismann[1] and Driesch.[2] In spite of all the criticism levelled
against his theories, and although my personal views differ in
many respects from his, I feel impelled here to emphasise the
epoch-making importance of Hans Driesch. It was he who
made the problem of form the cornerstone of all biological
theory. It is due to him that the genesis and development of
the individual occupies its central position in biological
thought. To see his importance we have only to think of the
influence his teachings have had in the field of sociology.
From the historical standpoint it is possible to divide biological
theory into pre-Driesch and post-Driesch periods. Through
Driesch the human mind has been confronted with a new set
of problems. His greatest and most permanent merit lies in his
having provided a new experimental and theoretical foundation for the concept of wholeness and in his having made it the
centre of general interest.

August Weismann is the other great theorist who at the

[1] 1892, 1902. [2] 1928a, etc.

beginning of the century gave new direction to mechanistic thought. It is true that mechanism was already flourishing at the turn of the century as Darwin's theory of descent had become widely known. Yet it was not Ernst Haeckel (1866), as is popularly supposed, who subjected to critical examination all the current knowledge and hypotheses regarding organic form. It was Weismann (1892) who did this. He added greatly to these facts by his own researches and, after collecting and collating all that was then known, he formulated his mechanistic principle of development. It was Weismann who gave Darwinism its precise theoretical foundation, for Darwinism is not evolution *tout court* but the theory of the part played by natural selection in producing new species.[3] Weismann produced a theory of heredity and a theory of ontogenetic development. The full significance of these two great names is apparent in the fact that the controversy carried on in biology since their time is in part a continuation of that begun by Weismann and Driesch.

2. WEISMANN'S GERMPLASM THEORY[4]

Weismann regarded the development of the egg into the completed organism as the becoming visible of a complexity latent in the egg. His views are generally referred to as his germplasm theory because the various parts of the body are simply developed—they were there already, but invisible.

The egg cell has the potentiality of forming the whole body. The cells produced by the fission of the germinal cell loose this "omnipotentiality" in becoming body cells. The only exceptions are the germ cells. These do not share in the activities of the body but remain dormant until the time comes when they can fulfil their special function, i.e. fertilization and the formation of a new and whole body. The body cells, on the other hand, have meanwhile undertaken the task allotted to them, and have thus developed all the potentialities they were given.

The egg cell with its universal powers produces two sorts of

[3] C. Darwin, 1859.   [4] 1892, 1902.

cell: (a) cells like itself which constitute the germplasm, and (b) somatic cells which are given specialized bodily functions.

According to Weismann then the development of the individual, or ontogeny, consists therefore in the large-scale change of germplasm into body cells. Thus most of the descendants of the original germ cells form the body, or soma. A small residue of the germplasm remains unaffected, and from this the gametic cells are formed. It is obvious then that this germplasm continues unaltered throughout the life-history of the organism, producing in each generation new cells which produce the body tissues. There is no continuity between the body cells of one generation and those of the next. On the other hand, the germplasm is passed on direct from the parents to the children, and is then handed on by them to the grandchildren and so on. The somatic cells disappear *in toto* with the death of the individual, but the germplasm lives on in the descendants. Its life is continuous over the generations; it is in a sense immortal. These are the essential points of Weismann's theory of the germplasm.

Lysenko (1948) recently branded this theory as idealistic. This obviously realistic theory, however, has done much to further the teaching of mechanists and materialists. Its advantage is that it clearly separates the germplasm from the somatoplasm.

Weismann's theory is founded on logical postulates which can be deduced from the facts, but the question which now arises is: where is this germplasm to be found? Is there anything in the body which satisfies these claims? Basing his views on the data collected by Strasburger, Boveri, O. Hertwig and others, Weismann (1902) thought he had found the material elements he required in the nucleus of the cell. As the cell nuclei of the whole organism are all derived from the nucleus of the fertilized egg-cell, the potentialities which become manifest in the separate cells must be latent in this ovum-nucleus (fertilized, in the case of sexual reproduction, and unfertilized in the case of parthogenesis). But what justifies his assumption that the germplasm is latent in the nucleus?

And what constituent of the nucleus is concerned with this? In the formation and heredity of the offspring the contribution of the father is just as important as that of the mother, though the mother generally contributes vastly more material than the father. The theorists, therefore, had to look for something contributed by father and mother in equal quantities. This could be nothing other than the nucleus, because the spermatozoon or male cell consists merely of a nucleus along with devices which facilitate its entry into the ovum. The tail of the spermatozoon, which enables it to move, is usually left outside the ovum, or egg cell, when fertilization takes place. Thus the germplasm demanded by this theory must be contained only within the nucleus, i.e., in its chromatic material— the very important substance seen in the process of cell division. This seemed the more probable as the head of the spermatozoon consists chiefly of chromatin.

Basing his thought upon these facts, Weismann then considered the theory of natural selection in regard to its effect upon the germplasm. Any variation which can be observed in the individuals of a species must be caused by a corresponding variation in the germplasm. The organism does not acquire new forms as a result of some acquired characteristics being inherited, for this would imply that the somatic or body cells affect the germplasm. The cause of the tendency to vary is rather to be looked for in the variation in the germplasm. Since, then, the germplasm itself varies, and varies yet more because of its male and female components, the individuals of a species vary in accordance with the variation of their germplasm. Weismann demonstrated in numerous experiments the fact that the germplasm cannot be influenced by the soma. He vigorously opposed all the claims of the neo-Lamarckians. The individual variations which have their origin in the germplasm are either advantageous or disadvantageous in the struggle for existence and either help or hinder the organism possessing them. The organism possessing useful characters will thus stand a much better chance of passing them on to its offspring. In this way Darwin's hypothesis of selection was extended into a sphere in which it had a significance for animate things in the beginning of their ontogeny. Darwin (1859) had pointed to the effect and Weismann had pointed to the principle. Natural selection in fact begins in the germplasm. According to Weismann's theory, therefore, variations in the germplasm are inherited.

The "mosaic theory" is concerned with the heart of our problem. Roux (1893) originated this expression, but it is really a striking re-statement of Weismann's ideas of morphogenesis. It stimulated Driesch's criticism and led to the formulation of his theories. For us, it is the essential part of Weismann's hypothesis because it admits of experimental test. Weismann remained a convinced mechanist, and regarded the living organism, therefore, as a merogenous conglomeration of physical units. He was also one of the convinced classical determinists of his time.

The bodily organs must be pre-formed in the nucleus of the germ cell. Anything which happens to the cytoplasm of the germ cell is due entirely to the initiative of the nucleus. Seen under the microscope the nucleus has a granular appearance under certain conditions. Whenever a cell divides, some of the granular elements seem to appear as the chromosomes, the number of which is fixed for each species. As on each of these occasions all the chromosomes split longitudinally, and the resulting daughter chromosomes go in equal numbers to the two daughter cells, each of the latter then has one of each pair of the daughter chromosomes. Thus both daughter cells have exactly identical chromosomal material. Yet we have seen that in ontogeny the fertilized egg cell divides and of the resultant cells some become somatoplasm, as postulated by the theory, while the rest remain to form the germplasm of the new organism. If then we want to discover how the soma is formed from the egg cell we shall have to observe closely the processes taking place in the soma. What does go on? Nothing but simple cell division. Every chromosome, every nucleus and hence every cell divides. Cell division, therefore, must be the cause, or prerequisite, of the whole ontogenetic development. This, however, presupposes that two identical chromosomes originate from the division of a single chromosome. This, however, was not Weismann's view. Here lies the first weak link in his chain of proof. He (1902) was firmly of the opinion that heterogeneous elements result from these divisions, for how could it be otherwise? If it were not so, then according to his theory no organism with various kinds of cells could develop from an ovum. All we should get would be a multicellular egg each cell of which would be identical. In consequence of this a *deus ex machina* was postulated in the form of the so-called *determinant*. For Weismann this determinant was a material entity which gives the cell a quite definite character. It follows that all determinants must be gathered in the germplasm in the form of a mosaic, and, at every cell division, they travel further and further from one another until they remain at last in distinct parts of the germinal and somatic tissues. Of course, the granular material of the ovum would present a similar mosaic which should admit of direct optical demonstration. Observation proved, however, that this mosaic is divided in such a way that the separate parts are not separated and distributed in groups, to arrive at last in particular parts of the growing germ and soma. On the contrary, at every division, each part of the mosaic divides in such a way that every newly-formed blastomere (cell) receives the same mosaic. Hence Weismann's determinant cannot be identical with anything observable in the nucleus. We are, therefore, forced to call the determinant a hypothetical *deus ex machina*. The determinants must be contained in fertilized eggs somehow and somewhere, but they are not arranged in the form of a mosaic. They are later separated by, and in the course of, cell division and assigned to the various areas of the germinal and somatic tissues. We see from this how completely hypothetical this mosaic theory is: we can find no material substratum for the determinant.

The process, however, has been explained by which the ovum is progressively divided, and how the cells so formed are differentiated to form very different tissues, each of which acquires with its final functions the appropriate determinant. Thus, after a phase of cell division, a phase of histological differentiation sets in. Both phases are completely automatic. The development of each little part is rigidly determined, and it achieves this development with the precision of a locomotive covering a certain distance along the lines. Somewhat, however, is left over of the determinant mosaic which is not determined; it is from this indeterminate part that new germ cells of the developing organism are formed.

The mosaic theory may thus be summed up as follows: the distinct parts of an organism, *A*, *B*, *C*, develop from determinants, A^1, B^1 and C^1. In the development of an organism, therefore, nothing new is produced. What happens is that the invisible becomes visible: an unfolding or development takes place. This developmental theory is a magnificent structure with which no one can fail to be fascinated. The Mendelian laws confirm it to some extent, but the findings of modern genetics tend to contradict it in so far as the same chromosomes appear in every cell of the body. The hope that the determinants were real entities has certainly not been realized.

3. EPIGENETIC THEORIES

(a) *Methodology*

The theory of epigenesis did not originate from a theoretical disagreement with Weismann's germplasm theory but from definite experimental observations. It was an endeavour to devise a theory of universal applicability based on a large number of separate facts. With his experimental embryology, Roux had directed morphogenetic enquiry into new paths. At the time, this method was called "developmental mechanics". Rapid results were obtained by Herbst, Wilson and T. H. Morgan as well as by Roux.[5] The introduction of experimental methods after a period of descriptive and comparative study produced new points of view which will be briefly discussed below.

[5] Herbst, 1893; Wilson, 1925; T. H. Morgan, 1921; Roux, 1893.

(b) *Oscar Hertwig's Theory of Biogenesis*

Referring once more to the scheme mentioned in the last chapter, if an organ or cell A can be traced to a region of the germ A^1 and B, C and D to regions B^1, C^1 and D^1, then, if we accept the mechanistic theory, the following must be true: As A is derived from A^1, A^1 contains potentially what has become actual in A. Hence an ovum must contain as many form principles as potentialities, and these should develop automatically and independently of one another. Oscar Hertwig, the discoverer of fertilization, opposed this point of view with his own theory of "biogenesis". According to him, all the cells into which the ovum divides prior to any histological differentiation, i.e. the blastomeres, possess identical potentialities: the fact that in development only one of these potentialities is actually realized in each cell is due to the spatial grouping of the separate blastomeres. It is the situation of a blastomere relative to its sister blastomeres that determines whether one or another potentiality is actualized in a particular cell. O. Hertwig[6] was an opponent not only of mechanism but also of Darwin's theory of change, which he attacked in his book *Das Werden der Organismen* (1916). To express his standpoint we can use the terms of our scheme once more: In the formation of blastomeres, the foundation principles A^1, B^1, C^1, D^1 are distributed equally among all the cells. The fact that A, B, C or D becomes actualized in one or another cell is due entirely to its relative position.

(c) *Hans Driesch's Entelechial Wholeness Factor*[7]

Driesch's position was rather different, for his theory was based upon incontrovertible facts. He agreed with Weismann in holding that development is a gradual manifestation of a multiplicity which has its hidden foundations in the ovum. If, as Weismann assumed, the various potentialities, which were previously combined in the ovum, are shared among cells, the developmental powers become reduced as cell division

[6] 1875-8.   [7] 1928a and 1938.

progresses, Starting with the ovum as a single cell, it is possible, on this view, to indicate how individual organs, later to be developed, will group themselves as divisions proceed. With the first series of divisions the developing egg is divided into what will later form right and left halves, then into front and back portions of the body—just as Weismann (1892) had imagined. Gradually the various parts of the body become marked off as germinal layers and allotted their positions. This, or something very like it, is what happens more or less in the development of all animal embryos. If we now take the object of Driesch's (1928a) classical experiments—the sea-urchin's egg —we should expect that, according to the views expressed so far, once the ovum has divided into two cells, each of these would produce only a half of the complete animal, for each of the two cells should possess the power of developing one half of the body only. Driesch showed, however, that, when the two cells produced by the first division were isolated, each cell produced a complete animal. Further experiments along the same lines proved that such powers of accommodation were not confined to the sea-urchin, but extended to many other animals as well. Complete animals, it was found, could be obtained from the blastomeres formed at the four-cell stage of the division of the egg. Even when the egg consisted of many cells, it could be broken up into fragments from each of which a whole animal may be produced. Opinions differed as to whether the powers of regeneration possessed by fully grown plants and animals were to be regarded as extensions of the same property or not. We shall consider this later. In any case the "mosaic" theory was disposed of and the versatility of the blastomeres became a proven fact. Individual blastomeres possess all the powers contained in the original germinal cell or egg—as we should expect from the fact that each blasto-mere has identical chromosomes. Hence the parts of the mosaic are not distributed among the various cells, so that each has a different part of the pattern; each daughter cell has all the powers of the ovum or egg.

In normal circumstances each area of the germinal tissue is

responsible for the production of a particular organ. The parts of this tissue which in our scheme we labelled A^1, B^1, C^1 and D^1 develop into A, B, C and D; their development in this direction is predetermined; their importance lies in their future or prospective destiny. A "prospective destiny" is not the same as a "potential destiny". But for Weismann both were identical; for him A^1 could produce nothing but A—never, in any circumstances B. Experiments have proved, however, that while A^1 usually produces A exclusively, it can in certain circumstances produce B, C or D. It follows then that every section of the germ possesses many potentialities, not all of which are realized. In normal circumstances only a few of the potentialities latent in the blastomeres are realized in very narrow limits. Hence potential destiny has a much wider field of application in morphogenesis than prospective destiny.

We shall now have to alter our scheme. According to Driesch (1928) in the germ cell there is a factor P (potentiality) which is capable of forming a complete animal. When cells divide, this factor is shared equally among them. What is it, then, which determines in the cells the potentialities of producing, at one time, a minor part, at another, a whole animal? Whatever it is which thus actualizes these potentialities so that they produce a complete organism cannot be thought of as anything of a material nature. This P factor, whatever it may be, is unaffected by the purely mechanical division; it retains its character of wholeness, a fact which may be easily deduced from its effort to make whole something which is incomplete. It is this wholeness factor which compels the potentialities of the cells to generate parts of a whole. The wholeness factor, however, does not reside in the parts but is outside them; it remains whole though the material substratum is divided. It cannot, then, be something material; it exists outside matter and must be itself immaterial.

In this way Driesch turned an argument against the mosaic theory into a proof of the independence of life; in proving that an observed natural process has an immaterial cause, he refuted implicitly monist materialism.

In the early stages of the development of an embryo, for example, in the gastrula stage, it is possible to exchange parts of the germinal material without interrupting their normal development. For example, Spemann (1936), using the embryo of a salamander, exchanged cells which were destined to become the central nervous system with some which were destined to become gut membrane. But the result was not the development of a central nervous system on the gut, or gut membrane on the back. The surprising result was a perfectly normal salamander. When material for gut membrane was placed in a particular place it produced what was appropriate in that place, i.e. spinal marrow. Similarly the material for spinal marrow became gut membrane. This was striking evidence in favour of Driesch's theories. It is proof of the multiple potentiality of embryonic cells. From this multiple potentiality, what is realized is that which ought to be produced in a particular place. The total effect of the realization of separate potentialities is a whole. The wholeness factor must exist, therefore, outside the cells.

At this point a difficulty appears. As I said, the experiment succeeded when carried out at an early stage of embryonic development, i.e. up to the completion of gastrulation. Once this stage has been reached, things happen in the way Weismann (1892) had anticipated. Once the endoderm has taken up its final position within the ectoderm, the material for gut becomes gut and that for spinal tissue becomes spinal tissue, even if these materials are placed in the wrong position. Thus, before the completion of gastrulation, the parts develop into what is appropriate in the position in which they find themselves; after it, they develop in accordance with their initial determination or prospective destiny. This seems contradictory, especially in the light of the following considerations. If when the egg divided all the potentialities were equally distributed, the soma cells of the future animal should also contain these multiple potentialities. For all that, a skin or muscle cell of a salamander is quite incapable of developing into a complete salamander. Yet Driesch's line of thought is such that this very fact serves to support his solution. The material which has developed into muscle cells might originally have developed into something else. Owing to its location, it has become actual as muscle cells. In so doing it has lost its other potentialities. Now that one potentiality has been realized, the others have passed into oblivion. The evidence for this is beyond dispute. Moreover, a time factor is involved. For a time, each cell in the embryo has a multiplicity of potentialities; during this period it is awaiting the realization of one of them. Once this destiny is achieved the other potentialities can never become realities. Thus the existence of a cell or germinal region falls into two periods: that of multiple potentiality prior to realization, and that of development in the direction of a definite goal, once it is finally orientated towards that goal. The question is, when exactly this determination takes place. There appears to be a multitude of possibilities in respect to this point. In plants meristematic cells never reach this point of final determination; anything can develop from them at all times. But animals, too, appear to have cells which, though actualized for a special task, still retain the potentiality of becoming something entirely different. This implies that the actualization of one potentiality does not always lead to the extinction of all others. Here actualization does not correspond with determination. We shall consider this point further later in the book. Let us return now to Spemann's (1936) experiments in transplantation. We saw that before gastrulation was complete, cells were still versatile, while, after it, their destiny was fixed for good and all. We can thus agree with Driesch in concluding that the potential destiny of cells can become manifest only when this is technically possible.

M. Hartmann (1933) and Kühn (1941) made a very careful distinction between "mosaic" eggs and "regulation" eggs. The latter behave as we have just described, while the mosaic eggs behave in accordance with Weismann's predictions. The experiments of Wilson showed that an egg of this sort does in

7

fact behave as though there were present in it a mosaic of determinants. If the blastomeres of such an egg are separated, the half or the quarter of an animal does in fact result. Driesch (1928) met this difficulty by assuming that in this case a determination has already taken place in the various regions of the cytoplasm before cell division begins. If this is accepted, it means a lot more than a denial of the mosaic theory of Weismann and Roux. It entails a complete break with the theory of the germplasm. For, if Driesch's explanation of the mosaic egg is correct, "prospective destiny" and "potential destiny" are to be sought in the cytoplasm, not in the nucleus. We are once more confronted with the problem which appeared to have been solved by Weismann and his theory of heredity: What is the function of the nucleus and what are we to make of the nucleus of the male sperm? From this question many other questions arise. As regards the nucleus at least, scarcely any doubt remains, for its rôle has long been established by geneticists.

Driesch was careful to collect facts before bringing forward his explanation of the "mosaic eggs" and attacking the dominant rôle of the nucleus. Yet his solution still fails to satisfy us, especially as elsewhere Driesch constructed his second proof of the total independence of the life principle on the traditional concept of the nucleus and Weismann's theory of heredity. In any case, the debate now enters another field— the relationship between nucleus and cytoplasm.

None of what has been said, however, alters the fact that Driesch's researches and thought have weighted the scales in favour of epigenesis. The fact that some things do not fit in merely shows how necessary it is, here and elsewhere, to examine the limits within which any principle discovered applies.

The theory of epigenesis, then, declares that the elementary particles of an organism contain nothing but potentialities which are realized by a factor of wholeness—an immaterial image of the entire organism. Under the influence of this factor they combine to produce an integrated whole. Since a part of this basic material can also produce a whole, the operative factor must be a principle of order which creates wholes. This must be so because the organism's wholeness is unaffected by division of its material substratum. This factor must be itself immaterial, since the particles affected by it are the material which forms the organism.

(d) *Hans Spemann: Induction and Organizer*

To understand Driesch's point of view one must always bear in mind that Driesch was consistently opposed to Weismann's developmental theory. Yet the development of a whole organism can be explained in a way quite different from that of Weismann. It may be due to a correlation of the separate parts. Spemann (1936) and his school were concerned with the isolation and transplantation of separate parts of the salamander's germinal tissue. Spemann's main conclusion was that the ultimate product of any one part of the germ is due to its relationship with other parts. Driesch demonstrated the multiple potentiality of the germinal regions, and wondered why this potentiality was realized in the one way which would produce a complete organism. He himself visualized the cause as an immaterial image of the whole—the "entelechy". But could not the "wholeness factor" be some corporeal particle?

Spemann (1936) and his followers showed that if a part of the young developing organism (gastrula) was isolated in a medium and so separated from influences of the rest of the body, it developed in accordance with its prospective destiny; skin material became skin, and so on. Nothing transcendental, nothing outside itself, was necessary to realize its potentiality. In spite of any multiple potentiality it might possess, it developed automatically entirely in accordance with its prescribed prospective destiny. Such fragments, therefore, possess the power of self-differentiation. On the other hand, it was proved that the formation of certain organs takes place only in proximity to certain other organs. Their formation has to be induced—to use Spemann's term—by some other part of the body. When this happens, they are not necessarily formed in their usual position; their formation is absolutely dependent upon the proximity of the organ which provides the stimulus to their development. For example, the lens of the eye is a skin formation which does not occur if the optic cup beneath the membrane, which develops into the lens, is removed. If the eye is transplanted to some other part of the skin, however, a lens is formed over it. The conclusion is that skin is anywhere able to form lenses but does so only when induced to do so by an optic cup. Thus there are two opposed principles at work which bring about differentiation, self-differentiation and differentiation by an external factor. Holtfreter (1932) proved that a chemical stimulant is here at work, by showing that the lens was still formed even when the eye which induced it was destroyed.

Spemann thus distinguished between two systems which are correlated: (1) an "action system" in which a previously determined development occurs automatically, and (2) a "reaction system" in which a definite development is stimulated. By this means, the effects of the transplantations previously mentioned were explained; a graft into a new environment is moulded and determined in accordance with this environment. Research by Spemann and Hilda Mangold (1929) revealed another fact of importance. It had already been observed that grafts to a new position did not invariably develop into what was appropriate to this position but sometimes developed in accordance with their position of origin. It was, however, supposed that for some reason or other their determination in one direction or another had already taken place, so that the grafts behaved in their new positions as they would have done in the old.

As early as 1901 Boveri had guessed that there might be special spheres, localized regions, from which all the surrounding regions were influenced and given their specific form. It became apparent that grafts in certain cases not only developed on lines dictated by their origin, but also caused the surrounding tissue to be modified along the same lines; the result was that the graft, along with the surrounding regions of the gastrula though still in their original situations, yielded a complete complex of organs.

The dorsal side of the primitive lip of a gastrula normally gives rise to the upper layer of the dorsal primitive gut, the notochord and the foundations of the mesoderm—the future spinal column and body cavity. Now if a piece of this tissue is removed and placed under the gut membrane of another germ, even of another species, the effect is not only the development there of a notochord, primitive spine etc. out of the graft but the surrounding tissue is induced to share in this formation of organs. In fact this participation extends so far beyond the framework of the middle fold of the gastrula that it induces in the ectoderm over it the development of a medullary plate, which then unfolds into a groove and ends in the medullary canal, the foundation of the spinal cord. The result is an embryo which has, under the gut membrane, in addition to its own normal one, a second set of organs proper to the back, i.e. notochord, primitive vertebrae and spinal marrow. It is clear that though we have here the interaction of several areas of the gastrula, the influence of a unifying principle is absent. A multiple action system exists which serves to induce the appropriate development in the various body parts.

If the experiment is repeated using different embryos first inserting under the gut membrane, in the same position, a fragment of the covering of the primitive gut from the front and then a piece from the back, the former induces a head— brain, eyes, ears—just as it would have done in its original position, while the latter brings about the formation of a body with spinal cord, tail and even fin fringe. The origin of the new and superfluous axial organs could occasionally be recognized as a composition of host cells and graft.

Driesch's theory is seriously contradicted by these facts. Driesch, as we saw, postulated a factor—an immaterial factor of wholeness—which aroused the potentialities of the single cells. Spemann and his school were able to show first, that the potentiality can become actual automatically as self-differentiation, and that, secondly, correlated with this, the awakening of a potentiality is due to an organizer which is represented by the whole of the action systems in the various distinct areas of the young embryo.

This organizer had no place in Weismann's developmental theory. For Driesch it was an entelechy tending to wholeness; for Spemann it was a network of stimulants which brings about the development of the organism in its separate parts.

This discrepancy between these views constituted the point of departure for the extremely profound researches of Hedwig Conrad-Martius (1944), which led finally to a synthesis with the teaching of traditional philosophy, and a view of the universe based on the broadest possible biological foundations.

(e) *Alexander Gurwitsch's Theory of an Embryo Field*

Gurwitsch (1927) saw a living organism as a field in which formative forces are at work which tend to create wholes. He distinguished between these forces and the materials upon which they work. The "dynamically preformed *morphe*" realizes itself in the embryonic material. Gurwitsch's observations were based upon studies of a much larger number of organisms than those of Driesch but his views are essentially the same.

(f) *P. Weiss's "Field of Determination"*

Weiss's[8] researches were more concerned with regeneration than with embryology, but he thought the processes of regeneration and morphogenesis were homologous. Weiss, then, is definitely opposed to Weismann and partly to Driesch. Weismann explained regeneration by assuming the existence of undeveloped germplasm of multiple potentiality. This he called "reserve plasm". Weiss agreed with Driesch in believing in a system based on harmony between equal potentialities. Weiss divided his system into two parts: (1) "the field of determination" which is in some way its foundation, and (2) the "circle of operation", the manifestation of the system in particular objects. We shall encounter this idea again and again.

[8] 1924, 1926.

(g) *The Gradient Theory of Boveri and Child*

In the course of its development, the blastula separates into a number of layers which behave towards one another in different ways. As far as we can see, the blastomeres should all turn out alike, for after all the egg and its potentialities are being shared equally. However, even in the ovum, an animal and a vegetative pole can be distinguished. In consequence, the blastomeres exhibit more animal or more vegetative characteristics according to their position in relation to the poles. Near the vegetative pole their character is most strongly vegetative, and the further they are from it, the more they lose this character until at last they are so little vegetative that they can no longer carry on with gastrulation. In 1901 Boveri spoke of a gradient leading gradually from one pole to the other. The gradient can be thought of as a series of layers through which the effectiveness of one pole becomes gradually weaker while that of the other becomes stronger.

As divisions occur the different cells go to the separated layers; each cell lying on a meridian is distinguished from its neighbours by its greater or smaller distance from one pole or another, by its "polarity", more or less strong. Boveri is clearly dealing with some primary structure immanent in the ovum. Hoerstadius's experiments with sea-urchin's eggs confirm this hypothesis at many points. In these experiments the developing egg was broken up into a series of rings of cells. These revealed a gradually increasing or decreasing tendency, from the apical or animal pole to the oral or vegetative pole, towards certain functions of the embryonic development. Cells which were purely animal were incapable of gastrulation. That in this case some interior function of the cell was at work appeared from the fact that, with the addition of vegetative cells, animal cells gained the ability to gastrulate. Thus the researches of Hoerstadius (1935) linked up with Spemann's theory of organizers.

Child (1924), the next biologist with whom we wish to deal, based his ideas on the researches of de Beer and Huxley into the early development of the fertilized egg. The animal pole of the egg is poorest in yolk, and a definite spot, the "grey crescent" (in amphibians), which later becomes the lip of the blastopore, lies right opposite the point at which the sperm entered when fertilization took place. Gastrulation begins at this grey crescent. These two points therefore must play an intensely active part in metabolism and must therefore be specially privileged. As the intensity of metabolism declines gradually from these points in all directions outwards, a primary differentiation is the result, and this induces the initial stages of development. The two layers of cells known as the germinal folds become correlated by this means in different ways, and thus a further stage of differentiation takes its origin. In spite of its very clear derivation from his own hypothesis (1936), Spemann found very serious objections to Child's.

IV

THE INDIVIDUALITY OF THE CELL

1. THE CELL AS THE UNIT OF THE LIVING FORM

THE great advances in our knowledge of morphogenesis result from detailed studies of sea-urchins and amphibia. We shall get a new angle on the subject if we direct our attention to some very different examples. If we accept the view that the entelechy or organizer is active creatively or as a stimulant, what is it? Let us put it another way round, and ask on what the activator acts and what the field is in which its operation can be established.

When Schwann (1839) and Schleiden (1833) enunciated the cell theory, they thought the cell was the physical unit of life. This was a mistake because the cell itself manifests all the qualities possessed by a complete organism. Nevertheless it seems abundantly clear that the cell is the unit of the living form. The cell behaves, then, in many ways like an organism. This is particularly evident in the case of unicellular organisms. The views of the earliest biologists who studied the protozoa make this very clear. Ehrenberg (1838), for example, was of the opinion that infusoria were quite like the multicellular organisms in consisting of numerous organs, and differed from them only in being microscopically small. Dujardin (1841) after a long controversy was able to convince his opponents that these minute animals were constructed entirely of a simple homogeneous mass which was called sarcodic material.

Of far-reaching importance was the discovery that this sarcodic material was homologous with the protoplasm of the cells of a multicellular organism. This meant that the whole body of an infusorian was on a level with a single cell of one of the higher animals. At one time a cell appears as a complete living being; at another it is just a component of a very complex one. It appears that it is the cell which is alive, and that the cell is the form in which life becomes manifest. When Pasteur (1862) proved that no one had demonstrated that living matter could arise from non-living and non-cellular matter the consequence was inevitable: where there is life, there are cells. Nowhere is it possible to find life without cells. When it was demonstrated that the egg is also a cell, the expression *omne vivum ex ovo* could be generalized as *omne vivum e cellula*. This meant, too, that all organic compounds occurring free in nature, if coming from living creatures, were traceable to cells. If we accept as proved the fact that cells are the distinguishing mark of life, various theories as to the origin of life can be disposed of. If, like Richter,[1] we assume that life reached the earth from another star, this life must have come as cells, and may still be coming. But where in the universe have these arisen? "Germs of life"—whatever these may be—are quite unknown to us. We know only cells, and we know that these exist only in given conditions, which are certainly absent from interplanetary space. But without cells there is no life. We have plenty of non-living matter on the earth but we cannot explain how a cell came into being from it. Preyer (1880) held the view that life came directly from the glowing heat of the heavenly bodies; non-living matter is merely the slag of this living process which continues to glow only in living beings—and, of course, in the earth's interior. If this is so, we can only say that this "glow" is in no way comparable with the life which the cell alone exhibits. The existence of the cell, and therefore of life, is possible only in certain conditions which are present neither in the cold of interplanetary space nor in the white heat of the fixed stars. Biology is not concerned with any other sort of life.

The cell, then, is the functional and formal unit of life. Life is a function of the cell; life is thus the expression of the cell's nature, and the cell is the form in which life manifests itself.

The term "functional unit" simply implies that the cell mani-

---

[1] 1865 and 1870.

fests the fundamental properties of life, viz. metabolism, change of form and irritability. The phenomena observable in a multicellular organism can be analysed into those exhibited by the individual cells. On the other hand bits of a cell do not exhibit phenomena which if added together would explain its functioning. Altmann's[2] attempts to break the cell up into granules were a failure. Verworn's[3] biogenes are only hypothetical entities. It is difficult to doubt the existence of Nägeli's (1862) micells, but there is no proof that they are capable of any independent existence. Earlier it was pointed out that a living organism may occasionally produce fibrous structures capable of an independent existence; this, however, does not affect the point of view expressed above, because such formations are the direct result of cell activity.

The conclusions we have now reached necessarily raise two important questions:

1. If a cell cannot arise directly from lifeless matter, are there no preliminary stages, is there nothing of the nature of Haeckel's "primeval slime", in other words an "ante-cell" which does not as yet possess all the functions of a single cell? Haeckel (1866) wrote of "flakes" of living primeval slime, capable of movement and metabolism, but having no structure and therefore not cells.

2. Apart from the fact that speculations of this sort have always proved to be baseless, cannot we regard those bacteria which have no nuclei, or possibly the viruses, as something of the nature of Haeckel's primeval slime?

In this connection a system of classification devised by Storch in 1948 is of interest. Storch distinguished several levels or stages beginning with the hypothetical pre-cells:

    1. Acytaria (viruses) which possess no cellular structure.

    2. Protocytaria (blue-green algae) which show no differentiation into cytoplasm and nucleus.

    3. Cytaria, which include all other plants and animals whose nature is explicable in terms of cells.

---

[2] 1890–4.   [3] 1888 and 1890.

4. Hypercytaria—human beings who, though cellular in structure, cannot be satisfactorily explained in terms of cell contents or cell functioning.

From this it is clear that one level is not to be explained merely by reference to another level. Man's peculiar position is underlined. Nicolai Hartmann (1940) pointed out that while one level of being necessarily presupposes another, it does not necessarily depend upon it.

The viruses do not possess the (normal) form of a living body: viruses are not composed of cells at least in the ordinary meaning of the word cell. Does this mean then that there is a form of life which is non-cellular? If it does we shall have to prove that the virus is alive. But what do we mean by saying a thing is alive? We know a thing is alive when it behaves in a certain way, carries out certain functions, but there are few, if any, functions or modes of behaviour which are possessed by all things which are said to be alive. If, for example, we make reproduction a criterion of life, then we find that auto-catalytic enzymes can reproduce themselves. All animate things, however, show some form of heredity so far as we know. Viruses undoubtedly possess some of the features of other animate things. A single virus infects a host cell and causes the host to assist in its reproduction, so that as far as a bacteriophage is concerned, for one bacteriophage infecting a bacterial cell, a hundred descendants are produced and the bacterial cell is disrupted in the process. Normally all these descendants are replicas of the original infecting body. The phage has reproduced itself exactly. But sometimes some of the resultant phages are different from the parent one. These are called mutations. By multiple infections of different phages genetic recombinations of "genes" in the phages may be produced; that is, "hybrids" are formed. In other words the viruses show a type of heredity and linkage groups have been demonstrated in some of them. No inanimate thing, no enzyme, could conceivably exhibit heredity, that is, a precise heredity of differences shown in mathematical ratios.

On the other hand, so far as we know, no virus is a free

active body. Viruses only become active when inside a cell which is already animate. Viruses must, however, exist outside cells but they are then inactive. They may even become inactive while within cells and remain in many generations of the cells until sooner or later some of them become active again and begin to reproduce and destroy their host cell. Chemically viruses are composed chiefly of nucleoprotein and nucleic acid. Thus they possess the chemical which seems to be basic to all animate things. By means of certain shock treatments it has been shown that some viruses possess an outside membrane or wall of protein and within which the nucleic acid is contained. But they are not cells in the ordinary sense. They could be imagined as extremely simplified cells possessing only the absolute essentials necessary for a parasitic form of existence and able to exist in an inactive state. Some authorities consider that they are animate and others think they are inanimate things. Some people contend that at this molecular level the word "living" has no meaning for either the biologist or the biochemist. Perhaps the viruses cannot truly be said to be either animate or inanimate—another category of description may be necessary. These things create a problem for the biologist and philosopher alike, but as research proceeds it is becoming clear that ultimately the viruses will be found to be a non-cellular form of life functioning only at the biochemical level and as such they could be autonomous structures, or animate structures on the way to becoming cells, or degenerate structures which have lost their cellular nature. It still remains true, however, that for the vast majority of animate things "the cell is the form in which life manifests itself".

As to the other argument in favour of a transitory stage—that based on Haeckel's living "flakes" of primeval slime—the organism *Pelomyxa palustris* is here involved. This is an amoeba which is in every sense animate. The assumption that *Pelomyxa* is a structureless slime lacking cell-nuclei is quite wrong. Rather is it a giant amoeba with not only one but a vast number of nuclei, though admittedly it is hard to render these visible. As for the bacteria, Piekarski (1937) has proved that the rod-shaped bacilli have as many as two nuclei. Their content of nucleoprotein is demonstrated both by staining and by the reflection of ultra-violet light by the Casparsson method. These nuclei divide, too, with every division of the body; in fact it is their division which initiates the division of the whole body. If anyone is still disinclined to regard these as nuclei, he should bear in mind that nucleoprotein and nucleic acid are considered to be the most important constituents of the nucleus. Reichenow's (1928) extremely valuable studies of the nature of nucleoli in the nuclei of protozoa provide us with adequate proof of this.

On the other hand, the situation in regard to the blue-green algae is far from clear. This problem and the other raised above will be treated in more detail below.

2. NUCLEUS AND CYTOPLASM AS FUNCTIONS OF THE CELL

There is no doubt that the blue-green algae have no organized nuclei.[4] Yet they exhibit all the vital functions of other cells and their forms are very like those of the green algae; they divide and are capable of assimilation, etc. The fact that, as far as I know, sexual processes have not been observed in blue-green algae should not disconcert us; these processes have not been discovered in amoebae either, except in the case of *Amoeba diploidea*, which very probably possesses a nucleus. If, however, one sees in the sexual act a necessary mixing of substance and characteristics, a sort of introduction of new blood, one should not forget the numerous plants and animals in which self-fertilization is the rule. We are perfectly justified, therefore, in regarding the body of the blue-green algae as a cell, since, though lacking an organized nucleus, it is quite like other cells in every other way. We seem to have a case here of life without a true nucleus. The immense importance of the organized nucleus has been proved in the case of many other cells, and one would naturally expect a cell without such

[4] It has been shown, however, by means of various dyes that blue-green algal cells possess chromatic material in the form of threads or a network, and these threads change cyclically as the cell divides.—Editor.

a nucleus to behave differently. Yet this is not so. How is this anomaly to be explained? Are there some form-elements in the cell, the importance of which is equivalent to that of the nucleus?

One thing is certain—the cytoplasm can never regenerate a nucleus which has been lost, and a nucleus is always produced solely by the fission of a nucleus. The cytoplasm, therefore, has no power to produce a nucleus. It would appear, then, that a nucleus can be represented by nothing else, for a cell deprived experimentally of a nucleus perishes. Are we right in thinking that, where a nucleus is lacking, some counterpart exists, which is generated by the cleavage of its like, which cannot be formed from cytoplasm, and which is functionally irreplaceable? Max Hartmann[5] speaks of certain autonomous cell elements which fulfil these requirements.

One of these elements is the centrosome, which Hartmann calls the "locomotive component" of the cell. This element occurs in all animal cells. It initiates cell division by itself dividing into two. The two resulting products draw out the nuclear spindle, through the agency of which the daughter chromosomes are then separated from one another. Thus the centrosome is considered to control the division mechanism of both nucleus and cytoplasm; the two poles of the nuclear spindle are "attached" to the two granular centrioles, or the indistinctly spherical centrosome, and the chromosomes are clearly subjected to some attracting force. These structures are found in all animal cells, but their forms are rather variable. In cell division these structures seem to initiate the formation of the spindle. Thus, in a sense, they appear to be the driving force behind mitosis. A similar process of mitosis occurs in the cells of the higher plants; chromosomes and spindle occur, but the centrosomes—the motivating factors in animals— appear to be lacking. The recently discovered "polar caps" which look quite different from centrosomes are thought to be produced from karyolymph or nuclear sap which diffuses

[5] 1932, 1933.

through the nuclear membrane. Their function, however, is the complete counterpart of the centrosomes. If we study the excellent monograph on cell division by Belar[6] we shall discover extraordinary forms of mitosis occurring in the nuclei of protozoa. We shall find things which are unlike both centrosomes and polar caps and yet perform exactly the same functions as these. If the centrosome is defined simply as the device which produces the movements, a centrosome is found everywhere, though its form differs widely.

The other cell element of this kind is the plastid. The plastids of plant cells are always associated with some metabolic function. In colourless cells they are found as leucoplasts concerned in sugar conversion; in cells exposed to light they develop chlorophyll, giving a green colour to the cells containing this substance and forming chloroplasts. Chromoplasts are cells which contain the orange and yellow pigments, carotin and xanthophyll, to which flowers and fruits owe some of their colours. Zumstein's (1900) experiments with *Euglena gracilis* showed clearly that these plastids are primary elements; no product of cell division can produce a plastid unless it has inherited one, but there is evidence to show that plastids may originate from other cytoplasmic bodies called mitochondria, which they resemble in chemical composition. The blue-green algae carry out photosynthesis, but they do it without chloroplasts. The chlorophyll, which is accompanied by a blue and sometimes a red pigment as well, occurs in every part of the outer layer of the cytoplasm.

So the blue-green algae possess neither organized nucleus nor chromatophores and yet everything proceeds as it should. If in one case the pigment is carried in the whole of one layer of the cytoplasm and in another by certain granular structures, it remains a fact that the cytoplasm is the primary bearer of the pigment. The granular structures are parts of the cytoplasm which have become specialized for this function. Perhaps the same may be said of the nucleus and the centriole. These, too,

[6] 1926a, b; 1928.

are specialized parts of the cell. The work is done in either case. In the one case it is done by the whole or a part of the whole mass, while in the other it is performed by an element of the mass which has become specialized for this special function.

The point of view expressed above was enunciated similarly by Guilliermond in 1908 in respect to the bacteria, where chromidial nuclei are in question. The nucleus, therefore, must be considered merely in regard to its functions.

The dictum that there are no cells without nuclei still remains true for the vast majority of organisms; cells have either fully organized or diffuse nuclei. This conclusion is so inescapable that no empirical proof, chemical or otherwise, is necessary. It happens that in the case of the blue-green algae we can show that the nuclear material—the nucleoprotein, the chemical substance which is characteristic of the nucleus—is present in a diffused manner; while the whole virus body is chiefly composed of nucleoprotein but this body is not a cell in the ordinary sense. We make this point, be it emphasized, *sine ira et studio.*

Chromatin is a substance in the cell or nucleus which stains with certain basic dyes. Feulgen's reagent is generally regarded as showing the presence of chromatin. Biologically the chromatin is that material in the nucleus which develops to become the chromosomes. Chromatin, therefore, is functionally the hereditary material because the genes, or units of inheritance, are known to be carried on the chromosomes. Modern research, however, has shown that in the chromatin at certain stages parts stain with dyes and other parts do not stain. There are, therefore, two kinds of chromatin, euchromatin which stains lightly or not at all and heterochromatin which stains deeply. Generally the euchromatin is that part of the chromatin which contains the genes in the ordinary sense, although the heterochromatin shows some kind of hereditary activity chiefly by affecting the genes in its vicinity.

With the chemical analysis of chromosomal material that has now been made it is possible to say that the chief chemicals

8

present in chromosomes are deoxyribonucleic acid (DNA), ribonucleic acid (RNA) associated with the protein histone and other proteins. These nucleic acids and proteins form a complex called a nucleoprotein. It is the DNA which chiefly stains with Feulgen's reagent so that the test for chromatin is really a test for DNA. The difference in staining capacity between the euchromatin and the heterochromatin, noticeable during the resting stage of the nucleus, may possibly be due to a difference in the coating of nucleic acid on the chromosome in different regions of its length, although it seems to be more probably due to a differential coiling of the different parts of the chromatin or chromosome.

While Feulgen's reagent is regarded as a specific test for the presence of DNA, it is not the only one which can be used, but we do not need to mention any other here.

In most organisms chromatin seems to correspond with nucleoprotein, but perhaps this is not invariably true. For example, *Eimeria gadi* is a parasite which lives in the swimbladder of shellfish. This organism has normal nuclei and divides in the ordinary way, yet so far no nucleoprotein has been shown to be present in it. Again, the lampbrush chromosomes, which are found in developing oocytes of vertebrates with eggs containing yolk, are true chromosomes, but those of the salamander do not seem to contain nucleoprotein. On the other hand, the blepharoplasts of the sickness-producing trypanosomes, which are organelles related to the centrioles and to the flagella, are Feulgen positive.

Bearing these points in mind, then perhaps we may distinguish between chromatin and nucleoprotein by considering that the former refers to a function rather than to a definite chemical, while the latter is chemical. To sum up then, nucleus and cytoplasm correspond to different functions of the cell. The nucleus is usually quite distinct, but cells which give no optical evidence of a nucleus must be regarded as homologous with those that do. Furthermore, a part of the cell which has been carefully analysed—the chromatin—may be regarded as functional normally with a background of nucleoprotein.

We must now consider the cytoplasm and nucleus separately. In a way the cytoplasm represents the basic substratum of the cell from which nucleus, centrosome and plastids, etc., are differentiated parts. As a result there arises, for example, a certain functional polarity between nucleus and cytoplasm. The cytoplasm would seem to be dependent upon the nucleus. That the nucleus is partly independent of the cytoplasm is shown by the processes of fertilization. In the lower organisms fertilization consists in the fusion of two complete cells when, after the two cytoplasms have mingled together, the nuclei fuse. But in the higher animals, the male sperm—which is no more than a nucleus provided with a tail to facilitate its movements as it seeks for the egg—penetrates into the cytoplasm of an egg, or ovum, fuses with the nucleus of the latter, and then initiates cleavage of the egg.

The following stages are distinguishable:

1. Viruses, problematical at the present, but which are conceivably nuclear in nature without cytoplasm;

2. Blue-green algae having no organized nucleus but nuclear and cytoplasmic functions carried out in the protoplasm generally;

3. The alga *Acetabularia* has a nucleus which carries out generative functions. Apart from this, however, the cytoplasm is capable of all other anabolistic functions usually reserved to the nucleus;

4. In the majority of most other plants and animals other functions besides the generative one are controlled by the nucleus. For this reason the cytoplasm of the cells of these organisms is incapable of living for long without a nucleus. Comparison with *Acetabularia* indicates what extra functions have been taken over by the nucleus. Klebs separated nucleus-free protoplasts in *Spirogyra* by means of plasmolysis, and found that these could form neither chlorophyll nor a cellulose membrane. Cells of amoebae and infusoria were cut into pieces, one of which had a nucleus and one of which had not. The piece with a nucleus was able to regenerate the lost part and live on as before. The piece of the amoeba cell which

had no nucleus was unable to produce the secretion which enables the pseudopodia to adhere to surfaces and "flow" along. The functions in which excretion takes place—metabolism and assimilation—were both impossible. These facts afford clear evidence that besides the generative component the normal nucleus has a secretory one. We can, in consequence, distinguish another category.

5. The infusoria have reproductive and vegetative functions separated in such a way that they are located in two functionally distinct nuclei.

Without the functions localized in the nucleus, then, the cytoplasm is incapable of continued existence.[7] This fact becomes more and more clear as the nucleus acquires further functions. On the other hand, isolated functions of the nucleus which are not correlated in some way with the cytoplasm are inconceivable except perhaps in viruses. All these functions are interrelated, and nothing but the combined working of all of them can be properly called life. A single function cannot be said to live, however small the particle of matter it occupies.

In the literature of the subject the cell is sometimes described as an independent though complex unit of life and sometimes (and without any transition) as a compound of such units. It is for this reason that I found it necessary to go into such detail to show that a cell cannot be broken down into smaller parts which can still be said to be animated.

3. GENE AND GENOM

Some of the latest biological works refer to genes as the ultimate elements of life, as though this were a self-evident fact. Schrödinger's (1947) well-known book *What is Life?* for instance, gives the following general impression:[8] since genes

---

[7] We should note that the sieve tubes of higher plants which are usually considered to be living, lack nuclei but possess cytoplasm. Each sieve tube, however, is in intimate contact with a companion cell which possesses a nucleus. Sieve tubes are transport cells and do not divide.—Editor.

[8] Incidentally, Schrödinger was a physicist not a biologist.—Editor.

may be regarded as molecules, they must have a molecular structure, and can be investigated by the mathematical methods which alone give exact results. Since, luckily, the genes alone are responsible for the coming into being of the living form, they form the ideal starting point for a really exact research into the nature of life. The gene-molecules set off a chain reaction which ends in a number of qualities or characters in the organism corresponding to the number of genes. Hence an organism consists of nothing but a sum of qualities which owe their existence to the catalytic initiative of the genes.[9]

If we accept this, we shall have to accept the following proposition as proved: I look for the cause of the rather inconstant and experimentally variable characters of the organism and I do not find them in the cytoplasm but in the nucleus. Since the effects of the genes can be clearly distinguished from one another as growth proceeds, the genes must be distinct and separate in reality. On the other hand, certain genes are found to be linked together. Genes, then, act in part independently, in part in association. Detailed research has revealed that the number of groups of genes present in the organism corresponds to the number of chromosomes there are. Furthermore, every kind of chromosome occurs twice in a diploid, or normal, body cell and only once in a haploid cell, i.e. in a cell prepared for fertilization. In the reduction division, which produces the germ cells, the diploid set of chromosomes is reduced to two single sets. In the process of inheritance, of any two possible and corresponding characters, each germ cell can only carry the gene for one of them. (The white or red colour of the petals in Mendel's experiment is an example.) In fertilization two single sets of chromosomes come together so that the resultant zygote again possesses a double set. In the production of hybrids, therefore, the correlation of hereditary factors from male and female parents is quite objectively demonstrable. Since, as we said above, the hereditary genes

[9] Schrödinger, however, did not say this.—Editor.

occur linked in the same number of groups as there are chromosomes in the particular species, it is perfectly obvious that the genes producing characters in the hybrid are localized in the chromosomes.

Linked genes, however, may become separated from their normal association and become positioned in another set of genes. Thus a gene may be re-situated and assert its effect from its new position. This process takes place during chromosome pairing in the reduction division of the cell. In this process pairs of opposite chromosomes conjugate and while they are conjugated corresponding parts of the two chromosome partners can be exchanged one against the other. Thus again we have a process which may be observed through the microscope: the exchange of parts of the two conjugating chromosomes produces an exchange of the factors of inheritance. This process is called "crossing-over" and the fact that crossing-over can be expected with some probability makes it possible to calculate the sequence in which the genes lie on the chromosomes, giving what are called "chromosome maps". It is also possible to determine which hereditary factor is a mutant one when sudden spontaneous mutations occur among a mass of inherited characteristics. Such mutations may occur in one or more factors quite independently of one another. Mutations can be handed down unchanged or may return to their original condition by a back mutation. Mutations can be induced artificially by various means which generally bring about a molecular disintegration or some other molecular change. Thus there is no doubt that mutations represent alterations in the factors of inheritance. The immense scope of such gene mutations is some measure of the importance of a single gene. In some cases, however, the effect of a mutation can be quite small. A gene mutation sufficed to turn the flowering plant *Antirrhinum majus* into a nondescript plant resembling a liverwort. The consequence of another in the fruit-fly *Drosophila melanogaster* is winglessness or loss of eyes. There are very many other effects produced by mutated genes.

Having given this outline of some points in genetics we may now perhaps consider what a gene is. By its behaviour it corresponds to a characteristic of the organism because it is the postulated cause of the appearance of the character in the organism. Mendel, who founded the science of genetics, postulated factors which controlled the expression of inheritance. If a flower had red petals then there was a factor for redness in the germplasm; if it had white petals there was a factor for whiteness in the germplasm and so on. This view, however, turned out to be too naïve. Nowadays the word "gene" is used for factor and this word has no settled definition which will satisfy all experimental genetical situations. Essentially a gene is a genetical concept or abstraction drawn from the practical results of genetical experiments. It is a locus or a point on a chromosome corresponding to something which is actually present in the chromosome. The deoxyribonucleic acid is that part of the chromosome which is chiefly concerned in heredity and the gene is probably some part of this molecule. It behaves as a particle and as an entity, but is influenced in its behaviour by its exact position in the DNA chain molecule, so that in one position it manifests one response, while in another position it manifests another different response. The various genes in the organism are not considered to act alone. One gene influences another gene, that is, there is action and interaction between them. The result of this action and interaction is the sum total of characters which we see in the growing and adult organism.

There is no doubt that genetics is one of the most exact branches of natural science. Its conclusions are among the most certain ever reached by science. In the genes, moreover, we have an ideal case of the integration of characteristics in the substance of the thing which expresses itself through its characteristics. Geneticists work along two lines: (a) the characteristics of the phenotype[10] are noted, traced to their hereditary origins and compared with others; (b) cytological studies reveal

[10] The phenotype is what a thing looks like.

the existence of minute but optically identifiable material particles. The direct linear connection between the particles and the characters appearing in the phenotype satisfy the research worker that, using two methods, he is observing one and the same thing, namely the gene; what he sees in the chromosome and what he sees in the phenotype are objectively connected in the gene. The results of such genetic research are most satisfying and provide an excellent example of the confirmation of scientific theory with facts.[11]

Up to this point I am in perfect agreement, but some biologists often go further. A living body, they say, consists of a sum of qualities based upon a sum of genes. The genes are genetically isolated in experimental results and they are held to correspond to something objectively distinct. This view is held in spite of the fact that there is increasing evidence of cytoplasmic inheritance independent of the nucleus. Nevertheless it is held that there are few genes outside the nucleus and so it is claimed that the genes are the fundamental units of life. To use the terminology I have adopted, a merogenous principle is here at work building up a merogenous system. Thus it is not the cell but the gene which is the fundamental element of the living form. The arguments of the preceding chapter will have shown that this conclusion is not justified, though it is commonly held. Let us now apply what we have so far learnt to the genes.

The whole genom, i.e. the merogenous sum of all the genes, is present in the cell nucleus in the form of chromosomes. These numerous genes are distributed among many cells by the process of cell division. In individual cells the genes proceed to realize those characteristics which are appropriate to their nature. The process is undoubtedly automatic and merogenous. Such a view can be described as genetic atomism.

Although every mechanist would regard this position as open to serious doubts, it is one which must be accepted if the

[11] The gene itself, of course, cannot actually be *seen*. What may be seen are chromomeres, or small lengths of chromosomes containing many genes. But the statement in the text expresses a truth.—Editor.

gene is to be given the rôle of the ultimate element of life. The only conclusion which can be maintained without question, is that the genes set off chain-reactions which are completed in the emergence of the various characteristics of the organisms. The remarks which we made above to the effect that the phenotype of the organism is the result of the action and interaction of all the genes in the nuclei, shows that the gene really is without significance except as part of the genom to which it belongs, whether we regard the genom as the sum of the innate characters, or as a whole set of chromosomes. While the gene may be treated as an isolated thing in a genetical experiment, and in fact, this analytic isolation makes genetical experiments possible, the reality in the chromosome which the gene represents cannot in fact be isolated from the chromosome, and examined like a chemical compound.

Even though the gene can be dealt with singly in experiments, this does not alter the fact that all genes in order to be effective must form part of a genom. One may be replaced by another, but no essential gene can be done without. This view is corroborated by the phenomenon known as "deletion". When mutations are induced artificially by X-rays, chromosomes break up into fragments. Such fragments can become attached to another chromosome and a "translocation" takes place. But such a fragment can also disappear completely. If this happens homozygotically, i.e. on both of the corresponding alleles of a gene-pair, this complete defection of a gene is lethal. On the other hand extra genes may be added, and in polyploid cells these may be numerous. Yet it is probable that the most important form-determinants must be present in the genom. The genom is therefore a mosaic of many genes and obviously a merogenous system.

Would it be true to say that the organism is a developed genom, and the genom an undeveloped organism? Although this is obviously not so, the truth of the matter does emerge inevitably from the rejection of this proposition. The genom —the sum of the genes—would itself be nothing but a definite number of different, even if precisely constructed, molecules,

What makes these molecules into a genom is the fact that they fit into certain chemical processes which then become a harmonious complex of characteristics. The genes may be regarded as catalysts which, in a chemical situation with many possibilities, initiate a very special one. In this sense it is quite understandable that each particular gene is the cause of a quite distinct characteristic. But what is the origin of the gene? If we agree that it came from another like it, a process of growth must have preceded it, for the genes originating from the genes of a parent pair are many times more numerous than those genes which were present in the fertilized egg-cell. Once more, then, the existence of a genom presupposes a chain of extremely complicated chemical reactions, all of which are linked with numerous necessary conditions within the organism.

The gene corresponds to something actual which owes its existence to a wealth of potentialities which led to its creation. But the gene itself is also a potentiality in that it brings about the realization of a character. Thus the gene is not an early stage of the character; it is simply a pre-requisite for its realization.

Now, to return to the main line of our argument, the cell's various parts are *actual*. They represent the necessary potentialities for its creation. Thus what was said in the last chapter is once more confirmed by our inclusion of the genes. It is not the separate constituents of the cell which live; it is only the cell, which is composed of these various parts, that exhibits the phenomena of life; the cell is the morphological element of life and its functional unit.

4. THE CELL AS AN ORDERED WHOLE

In the last section we established the fact that nothing less than a cell can be regarded as the unit of life.[12] A cell, it is

---

[12] As already noted, the case of viruses is problematical but their peculiar and exceptional form only serves to emphasize the argument advanced here. A virus is a merogenous whole and has a definite form although not strictly a "cell".—Editor.

true, is compounded of parts, but outside the cell these have a character and a behaviour quite different from those they exhibit when within it.

In considering what was meant by a chemo-dynamic process, we saw that in a definite field there reigned an order which we termed "life". This order consisted in the integration of chemical and physical processes. This is the order which we find in the cell. Seen as a chemo-dynamic process, life is a whole in which the parts, instead of going their separate ways, work together. The cell, once more, is a whole in this sense. The parts of a cell are recognized as its parts only in so far as they work together. To use a Kantian expression, the essence of "wholeness" consists in the "articulation" of the parts.

The existence of a cell depends upon the actualization of a twofold potentiality: (a) the "form" or order of the cell, and (b) the chemical laws governing the molecules. The relationship of these laws to the cell is purely passive. The operation of these laws could never by itself originate a cell. A cell becomes actual only through the principle of order reigning within it. This principle of order may be called the "active potentiality" of the material parts.

While the materials of which a cell is composed have an independent existence as well, this cannot be said of the "form" of the cell, which, as far as we are concerned, begins to exist only when its operation upon the chemical constituents becomes apparent. Thus our concept of the cell is, in the first instance, a purely abstract one. The cell is, however, something real. This is proved by the uniqueness of the laws which govern its activity. They exhibit a regularity which enables us to anticipate with certainty future developments in the living matter. Yet the "form" of the cell exists nowhere except in a real cell. Its existence concurrently with the chemical presuppositions may be recognized only in the rôle played by the constituent parts. The *forma cellulae* may be found only *in cellula*. The cell indeed is a concept, but a concept bound up only with actual things. All theories which ignore this introduce into the empirical sphere something which cannot be proved by empirical scientific means. No cell can derive its organization as a cell from any other source than another cell, in which this objective organization already exists. Alexis Moyse (1948) called this the *Anfangsorganisation*, the "original organization". Because of this, and the fact that inanimate molecules seem incapable of forming a cell, the idea that the original cell at some time developed from something else, is very hard to defend. So far as we know, too, life never arises except from pre-existing cells.

Once a cell has this objective, three-dimensional existence, the nutritive materials which it absorbs find their way to the places allotted them by its organization. The molecules which go to feed it take up their appropriate stations and play the parts assigned to them by the already-existing organization. Although we never find the separate form elements of the cell outside the cell, the same thing applies *mutatis mutandis* to them, for each of them performs a function which is explicable only if other functions co-exist. Genes, as we have shown, are genes only in so far as they are components of a nucleus, and are fed by the substances incorporated in the cytoplasm. The nucleus, which is the catalysing centre of the cell, could not exist apart from the cell, for its catalytic activity seems to depend upon the metabolic connections it has with the cytoplasm. And if the nucleus exists to produce catalysts, this activity would be pointless if there were nothing upon which they could work.

Even the relative sizes of nucleus and cytoplasm are subject to the principle which governs the total order of the cell. This may be seen in the working of the nucleus-cytoplasm relationship discovered by Richard Hertwig (1902). This relationship is the cause of cell-division, because any discrepancy in the proportions of nucleus and cytoplasm tends to a restoration of equilibrium, and this is achieved by cell division. It is, however, very clear that the nucleus-cytoplasm relationship is part and parcel of the general cell organization. This is evident from experiments in the dissection of cells: whenever the relationship is upset, it is always restored. The same experiments prove that the polar differentiation in the cells of infusoria is in accordance with a definite order which is at all times maintained. Experiments carried out on the cells of protozoa show that isolated parts of a cell are incapable of life, that the cytoplasm in particular cannot live without the nucleus. Of special interest are the experiments conducted by Gruber (1885) upon the tiny trumpet-like creature called *Stentor*.[13] If this animal, whose shape is rather like that of a sugar loaf, is cut transversely, the long macronucleus, formed of balls arranged somewhat like beads on a string, is broken into pieces. The following results were obtained when this was done.

1. Each fragment was regenerated and formed a perfect unicellular animal, i.e. the anterior end, with mouth part and vacuole, reduced the mouth part and developed the whole posterior end so that a symmetrically perfect, though very tiny *Stentor* resulted. Similarly the posterior end developed an anterior end, and pieces that came from the middle had to form both anterior and posterior ends afresh. It is worth noting that there was not only a regeneration of what was lost; the whole creature was regenerated, and the parts remaining were modified in such a way that the form principle of *Stentor* was maintained exactly, though on a smaller scale.

2. In spite of the division, the general axis of the body was actively form-determining in the fragments. This is clear from the following facts. Not only did the anterior end regenerate a new posterior end in the direction of the lost part; the fragments from the middle produced an anterior end on the wound surface directed to the lost anterior end, and a posterior end on the wound surface directed to the former posterior end. The polar differentiation of the whole uninjured cell was retained as a tendency towards differentiation in the parts. Consequently this tendency must be an expression of the polar

[13] For allied work see also Balbiani, 1888, 1892; Nussbaum, 1886; Verworn, 1891; Hofer, 1890; Lillie, 1896, 1929; Johnson, 1893; Morgan, 1923; Provazek, 1903; Socholoff, 1924 and Gruber, 1885.

differentiation and not merely a correlation effect of the particles.

3. The nucleus-cytoplasm relationship was shown to be a pre-established principle of order. Cell fragments containing too small a piece of the nucleus perished. Those, however, which had too large a proportion of nuclear material re-absorbed the excess until the nucleus was appropriate in size for the cytoplasm.

Stolte's (1922) experiments with the same creature—*Stentor* —also revealed that the form of the nucleus and the demands made upon it have an ordered relationship, based upon the principle of wholeness. In conditions of cold, hunger, etc., when the intensity of life is reduced, the necklace-like nucleus consists of a few large "beads". When life is more active, in conditions of warmth, abundant nourishment, etc., the number of beads is increased, but their size is reduced. Thus the nucleus-cytoplasm relationship is preserved, but the surface of the nucleus is increased or reduced in accordance with re-quirements.

The expression "pre-established principle of order" is in-tended to imply only that there is a principle of order present. There is no implication that this order tends towards any unalterable stability. On the contrary there is a constant flow of events; what we can observe is a sequence of conditions and phases in the life of the cell. Of course, conditions and phases are no more than aspects of the cell under observation. The cell is changing from moment to moment and so it is possible to delimit its various states, but this delimitation is arbitrary. We find it necessary to explain one condition by reference to another which precedes it, but the different phases of the cell's life are integrated no less than the parts of the complete cell. Thus the reality and unity of a cell as a form consists in the fact that the presence of one part enables us to infer—with the certainty that comes of our experience of regularity—that the other parts are also present. This is what is meant by spatial form.

But, with the same certainty based on our experience of

regularity, we can infer from a nuclear spindle with an equatorial plate that a diffuse stage preceded and that an anaphase will follow. These are temporal members in a process and are integrated in an objective time form. Hence both form elements and developmental phases express the order which makes of the cell a unity. The two are distinguished as "space-form" and "time-form".

Let us consider for a moment the time-form. There is a certain alternation of phases in the condition of a cell which goes on as though of necessity. On the other hand we see, for example, that certain phases of development occur with regularity only when particular external conditions are present. It follows that in the first case the condition depends entirely upon powers inherent in the cell, while in the second, the condition results partly from powers outside it. The processes which are exhibited by the "time-form" of the cell may be called "phase series". Thus we can distinguish endogenous and exogenous "phase series".

Driesch (1928), we remember, described the pre-established form of the body as an entelechy and by this he meant the immaterial basis or cause of its form. This concept is directly applicable to the cell, and Driesch did so apply it. According to Aristotle entelechy primarily means the active principle which turns what is possible into what is real. The form, the activity and the changes of a living body are all expressions of this entelechy. We were able to prove that the cell is not formed by means of a correlation of molecules or form elements. Hence the Aristotelian concept of entelechy corresponds exactly with the principle of order, which we see at work making the cell into a whole. It is a principle of wholeness which forms a unity from parts which would otherwise go their separate ways. Thus a hologenous system is born. Such a wholeness factor is the final cause of events proceeding in the cell. In other words wholeness is both cause and effect; the ultimate goal is the cause which exerts its influence upon the process. The cell is thus the prototype of what we have described as a hologenous system. An entelechy is something which gives direction to a process, in this case, the living form of the cell, regarded as movement.

5. THE ORDERING OF CELL DIVISION

It is the entelechy which directs every movement of the cell, and the time-form is the expression of this entelechy. Cell division, too, must be directed by the entelechy. As the entelechy activates all that happens in the cell before division, it must originate the division. But what is it that is operative in the new daughter cells? Is there some transcendent entelechy which first dominates the parent cell and then operates in the two products of division? I think I have made it plain that the entelechy cannot be immanent in the molecules; but is it immanent in the cell as such? If it is, it divides with the cell.

The idea of a transcendent entelechy is supported by the fact that in the fragments of the cell the same form is operative as previously dominated the undivided cell. If this view is not accepted, and we postulate an immanent entelechy, how do we explain the behaviour of Gruber's stentors?[14] Were there in the *Stentor* as many entelechies as one could make pieces capable of regeneration? If Hartmann's energid theory is interpreted in a vitalist sense, entelechy and energid could be regarded as synonymous. But then we should have mono-energid mono-entelechial cells and poly-energid poly-entelechial cells. But if, in cutting up his *Stentor*, Gruber also cut up their entelechies as well these must have spatial existence and be capable of self-regeneration. What is here said about the cell must also apply to the separated blastomeres with which Driesch experimented.

But against this it must be said that the true mark of the entelechy is its obedience to law. We can recognize it only in the activity it exhibits in the field of its operations—the cell. Each cell lives independently of its fellows. There is no evidence whatever that there is any full-scale connection between the two new cells which result from a division. No philosopher

[14] Gruber, 1885.

knows of any place in which an entelechy could reside other than in its field of operation. It is only there that it is possible to recognize the laws governing it. These considerations lead us to the view that there are as many entelechies as there are cells, and that an entelechy is operative in each cell. The cell, then, divides as a result of the order which reigns in it. This order, therefore, operates in two different fields. Nevertheless, it is not possible to call the order, as such, either wholeness or entelechy. Nor is entelechy identical with wholeness. Wholeness is applicable to the entelechy only with the addition of the material parts which co-operate to form a whole. However, the question of what constitutes a substantial form may be postponed. All that we need say here is that order, entelechy and wholeness all find expression in the cell, but it will require much thought to determine the exact meaning of these concepts.

V

THE MULTICELLULAR ORGANISM

1. THE RELATION OF THE CELL IN THE CELL COMMUNITY

AMONG the protista one cell constitutes the entire organism. Such an organism is therefore explicable in terms of the cell. On the other hand multicellular organisms, animals and plants—the metabionts—are built up from a number of cells. How is the cell of such an organism to be defined? Since we have recognized the cell as the unit of life, such complicated organisms must be combinations of such units. Is the cell of a unicellular organism homologous with the single cell of a multicellular organism, or with the whole organism? The obvious answer is that morphologically the cell of a protist is equivalent to one of the cells of a metabiont, while physiologically it corresponds to the entire multicellular organism. In general, people do not attach undue importance to the solution of this problem, for, from the mechanistic standpoint, it does not matter much where the atomic forces—the only operative ones—are concentrated. Bertalanffy,[1] however, treats of the problem in detail, but concludes that the problem of biological individuality is impossible of solution. My own view is that one cannot avoid this question merely because of its difficulty.

If the protist is merged in the totality, thus losing its substantial being as part of a greater whole, it will have suffered what traditional philosophy calls a *privatio*. A comparison of the cells of protista and metabiont, however, reveals that both are optically and chemically alike; they both possess nuclei, centrosomes or their equivalents, etc.; cell division, characterized by mitosis, occurs in both cases. There is nothing here to distinguish them. The cell of a protist possesses all the func-

[1] 1932, 1949.

tions characteristic of life: reproduction, metabolism, growth and irritability. There are but two points which might serve as a basis for distinction.

These points, however, are bound up less with the character of the individual cells than with the relationship of the cells of metabionts one to another. Although all these cells exhibit all the basic evidences of life, they show wide differences of development. Many cells of multicellular organisms have lost the power to divide. Sexual activities are restricted to a very closely defined group of cells. But, though all the cells of metabionts originate in a single cell, in so far as they together constitute an organism, there are very considerable differences among the various members of the family of cells and these lead eventually to the division of labour so characteristic of multicellular organisms. In the cells of protista we do not find such division of labour or such enormous differences among the cells of the same family. Yet even here the cells of succeeding generations often differ greatly; sexual activities may be confined to quite precise stages of division. Many parasites are known in which one generation is concerned with the taking in of nourishment for the benefit of succeeding generations; these inherit as it were the stores of food. There is thus some justification for thinking that among protista, or, more particularly, among parasites, there is a division of labour among parents, children and grandchildren. In the cells of the metabiont this division of labour is seen in the same generation as well. How this happens will be discussed later. What is clear is that we are not concerned with an entirely new principle entirely unknown among the protista. Even in protista the biotope frequently produces cells which, though genetically identical, are quite unlike their parent. Hence the cells of metabionts differ from these only in being social. They are otherwise neither richer nor poorer than the solitary cells. Accordingly it cannot be said that they are superior to the cells of protista. The conclusion is that wherever cells are found, whether solitary or as the components of multicellular organisms, they are all structurally the same.

2. THE MULTICELLULAR ORGANISM—A COLONY OF PROTISTA?

(a) *The Cell of the Multicellular Organism*

It would appear from the correspondence of the cells of protista and metabionts that the latter are simply colonies of the former. This conclusion is supported by other evidence.

It is difficult to decide whether the flagellata are plants or animals. Among these creatures there are solitary forms which can assume different modes of existence according to circumstances. At one time the individual may be a tiny, highly-mobile animal which swims about by means of flagella. At another time it will dispense with these flagella and take up a purely vegetative life like that of green algae. It is possible for cell division or multiplication to take place in either state. In some cases the vegetative forms, the "palmellae", grow in long algal-like threads; this happens because the cells produced by cell division do not become separated from one another. Sexual conjugation occurs only in the less common flagellate condition. In this example we see a gradual transition from a unicellular existence to a multicellular plant-like state. In other flagellata the tiny flagella-bearing animals remain together in a shapeless mass even after cell division. In yet others the mass is no longer shapeless but a round freely-swimming disc. Others again form a multicellular stick with clearly defined anterior and posterior ends. Other flagellata consist of spherical creatures, multicellular in character, with a division of function among the various cells. In these creatures the normal vegetative cells with flagella are incapable of either sexual activity or reproduction, these functions being reserved for other cells. Here, as Pascher (1914) showed, we see the division between animal and plant kingdom fairly well marked. But what is of more interest to us is the fact that in the case above-mentioned any distinction made between an unco-ordinated mass of protista and a multicellular metabiont is purely arbitrary.

The secret of the colony of protista consists simply in the fact that after division the cells, instead of parting, remain together. All that is needed now is for the cells to arrange among themselves a division of labour and we have before us a metabiont. It would seem that all the complicated structures of the higher plants and animals result from a more and more intricate division of labour among the cells which live in association. At the same time, there is no fundamental difference between a colony of protista and a protist living singly, on the one hand, and between such a colony and a metabiont, on the other. If this is so, the unicellular organism is completely under the control of its entelechy, while the multicellular organism is merogenously controlled. The multicellular organization requires, it is true, entelechial units to build up the metabiont, but no other principle of unity is added to the cells. There is nothing in this theory which favours a mechanistic explanation, but it does suggest that the multicellular organism is not a unity, as Driesch affirmed (1928).

The view expressed above is, of course, no more than a speculation which seems reasonable in view of the correspondence between the natures of the cells in protista and metabionts, and the gradual transition from one to the other. If this speculation is true to the facts, the following presupposition must be true: With complete knowledge of all the parts that go to make a cell or of the molecules from which it is constructed, I could never foresee with certainty the cell as the net result of the interaction of these things; if, on the other hand, I knew precisely all the characteristics of all the cells of a metabiont, I should be able to grasp all the potentialities and realities of the metabiont. For the metabiont would be the sum of the effects of the cells composing it; the organism would be governed by no other laws than those which govern its cells. If, then, the single cell is made an element by the whole; if, as an element, it is really a subjective aspect which enables me to understand it, then the unity of the multicellular organism is determined by its cellular elements. Here then is the criterion for the truth of the statement made above. What we now want to know is whether the metabiont does show evidence of an independent system of order which differs from that of the cells which compose it.

(b) *The Ability of the Cells of Metabionts to live independently*

It is well known that pieces of tissue may be removed from a living organism, kept in a vessel for years and made to grow. From this it is obvious that, given a suitable environment, the individual cell does not require to maintain its connection with other cells. Given the correct temperature, oxygen, a solution containing the appropriate nutrient materials and a means of removing the carbon dioxide produced—conditions identical with those of the living body—the cells can maintain themselves and grow. The body, be it noted, has to afford to each of its cells the conditions which enable it to live. The body is no more and no less than the totality of its cells; thus the cells provide one another with the conditions necessary for their life.

In a drop of water a protist is bound up ecologically with an environment produced by other living creatures; these creatures are necessary to it on account of the conditions they produce. The cell of a metabiont is similarly dependent upon the environment produced by its fellow cells. This dependence is only indirect in the sense that the other cells produce the ecological situation necessary for the cell's existence. A vase of freshly-cut flowers affords a good illustration of this situation; quite a number of morphogenetic processes, such as the formation of buds and the opening of flowers, can occur without the co-operation of the plant as a whole. The fact that cuttings have the power of regeneration, the ability to form complete plants, shows that a single shoot, a mere portion of the whole plant, has powers of life independent of the plant as a whole. Death, too, is a fate which does not overtake all cells in the same manner and simultaneously. Death, I have emphasized, is the state of purely molecular existence which is opposed to life. If life, then, consists in the principle of wholeness, this wholeness must be sought in the individual cells and not in the metabiont as a whole. If it were true that the cells are alive in consequence of their belonging to a whole, and if life were a manifestation of the wholeness of a metabiont, the cells would die along with the whole. In fact, however, death is often a very gradual process, beginning with separate and localized partial processes. For example, when the heart stops beating, certain tissues continue to live, and die only as their individual needs are no longer supplied. This being so, we must see the death of a metabiont only in the death of its cells and in nothing else.

It is possible nowadays to remove for a short time important organs such as the heart, and to substitute for it an artificial pumping mechanism. The cells of the body do not perish, since the necessary environmental conditions are maintained by artificial means.

We can summarize all this by saying that in a metabiont the totality of the cells fulfils, directly or indirectly, the needs of the individual cell, just as the circumambient conditions supply the needs of a protist. The body is the environment of the individual cell. Linser (1948) regarded the whole complicated reaction and reflex system of metabionts as nothing other than a series of chain reactions between the separate cells.

(c) *The Merogenous Order of the Cell State*

For Hedwig Conrad-Martius (1944) and myself Spemann's achievements in 1936 had far-reaching significance. Spemann himself would go no further than the bare facts. Nevertheless no theoretical examination of the living form can ignore his results, for they have deepened our knowledge considerably.

Making use of our conclusions and Spemann's experimental data, let us now outline the development and possible destiny of the cell of a metabiont. The fertilized ovum is the starting point for every such development; its unicellular character enables us to equate it with the cell of a protist. It is said with justice that every metabiont exists in the protist stage as an egg cell. The egg cell at this stage has a whole mass of devices such as the food material or yolk to feed the later embryo, and facilities for making it possible for the fully-formed offspring to break out of the shell; in other words the ovum is potentially related to its numerous cellular progeny. Yet this fact is in no sense a contradiction of its nature as the cell of a protist. Among the sporozoa, for instance, there often occurs a giant cell laden with food reserves; it is inserted as a link in a chain of generations, and has, even when encysted, openings specially prepared for the escape of its products. An example is furnished by the sporoducts in the reproductive cyst of *Gregarinidea*. The individual spores drop into the most varied environments to which they adapt themselves as well as they can. The ovum itself disintegrates but the individual cells remain together and share a common destiny in the same environment. This destiny may be said to be "common" only because the cells remain together, but the individual cell's destiny varies because its position in relation to its sister cells is different. Moreover the yolk is divided unequally among the blastomeres and this causes differences in the frequency of cell-division. The mere fact that the cells have to share a closely limited space in different positions means that their fortunes are different. Many parts, as, for example, the apical pole or the "grey half moon" in the amphibian egg, are essentially different from other parts; the cells which happen to occupy this region of the egg are differentiated from the others in quite a special way. Nevertheless, in considering the fortune of a single separate cell, there is nothing apparent which distinguishes it from the fortunes common to all cells.

The nature of a cell, then, is determined to some extent by its position in relation to other cells. But another determinant is time: the temporal succession of the stages in its existence. There is such a thing as the time-form. A distinction has also been drawn between endogenously and exogenously determined processes. By an endogenously determined stage we mean one in which the preceding stage is not only the potential foundation of its successor but also its cause. The endogenously determined stage is the necessary consequence of the stage before it. Expressed in another way, both the passive and the active potentialities of such a stage are contained in the preceding stage. A stage is said to be exogenously determined when the potentialities for its development lie passive in the preceding stage until some external factor activates them. In the life of a cell every stage is usually the result of both causal principles.

We find all these ideas clearly exemplified in Spemann's experiments, and as this is so, we are justified in applying these principles of determination to the cells of metabionts as well. We conclude, therefore, that the cells of multicellular organisms are not essentially different from those of protista.

After the division of the ovum into distinct germinal regions the following possibilities are open to the individual cell:

1. *Self-differentiation:* the potentialities latent in the cell are automatically unfolded, i.e. germinal regions become automatically what they should be as a result of their hereditary tendencies. That this does happen is proved by the fact that auto-differentiation occurs in a medium which cannot affect it, as when the cells are isolated from other cells. This is clearly a case of an endogenously determined change.

2. *Self-differentiation together with external stimulation:* cells are differentiated not only in accordance with their immanent potentialities, they also urge their neighbouring cells to differentiation in the same direction. Cell *A* possesses the potentiality to become cells of the axial organs and causes, or induces, cells *B*, *C*, and *D* to join with it also in forming the axial organs. This again is a case of endogenous determination, but here the cell is active in producing effects outside itself as well.

3. *Passive differentiation brought about by external stimulus:* the cell is not lacking in potentialities but these await the stimulation coming from another cell. Here we have a case of exogenous determination.

When the cells are differentiated in isolation, there is perhaps a combination of modes 1 and 3. When such cells come under the influence of other cells, potentialities are awakened which would have lain dormant in a case of pure self-differentiation. If this is so, the cell has many potentialities some of which require no external stimulus while others do, if they are to be realized. In the germ of amphibia, once one potentiality is awakened, the others appear to vanish. Yet if we consider the regenerative powers possessed by amphibia and a large number of plants and invertebrates, we cannot help considering that the dormant possibilities remain and only await the stimulus of some external factor to become realities. Hence the endogenously-determined development of a cell depends on its not being checked by external influences. In practice, self-differentiation proceeds alongside stimuli coming from outside, for, in natural conditions, cells develop in accordance with their inborn tendencies and are assisted in this development by external stimuli.

In the life of protista we find what corresponds to self-differentiation in the development through which the protist has to pass according to the laws which govern its being. The endogenously conditioned phases of the development of a protist are in every way equivalent to what Spemann called self-differentiation. In the course of its life a protist produces material which passes into its surroundings so that these are influenced and changed in a very characteristic manner. The cell gives to the medium in which it lives a characteristic stamp. One has only to think of the success of bacterial life in a medium, or of parasites in a body fluid. In practice, the condition of the medium is a criterion of the very specific sort of life it has supported. Fermentation and attacks of fever are signs that a yeast or a malarial organism is alive and active; these signs are so characteristic that, without seeing the living cells, we can determine their species simply from the medium in which they live. Processes which are exogenously conditioned are also known. A cell is not only the producer of changes in its environment. It is simultaneously a product of that environment, for it responds in a specific way to it by definite morphological changes. *Euglena* can swim about freely as a flagellate; grown on agar it usually assumes a palmella form; in unfavourable conditions it forms a cyst. Thus every cell through its by-products is the originator of a situation operative within its medium or environment; when it responds to a situation it is to that extent its product. For a typical example of self-differentiation and external stimulation, the experiments of Moewus[2] afford one. He showed that tissue which had been isolated from the body could cause surrounding cells of the same kind to develop into male or female gametes.

In a community of cells, therefore, it seems that each secretes substances and so gives a particular quality to its surroundings; at the same time it is itself affected by the substances which it takes up from its surrounding medium. We are thus brought to the third possibility, i.e. morphogenesis brought about by external stimulation.

Every cell in a community possesses potentialities either many or few. In its development it secretes substances some of which have no effect on other cells, while others are capable of realizing certain definite potentialities in other cells. The cells destined to develop into mesoderm, "grey half moon" or micromeres in the sea-urchin are particularly "obstinate" in regard to their self-differentiation. The cells of the future ectoderm, on the other hand, are very open to external stimulants. Set free in an indifferent medium they become differentiated as skin, but under the influence of a stimulant they will develop into a nervous system or into the lens of an eye.

Any realization of a potentiality produces a whole chain of most complicated chemical processes. In the higher animals it seems that, as soon as one potentiality has been awakened and morphogenesis has taken a particular direction, all other potentialities are extinguished. Thus once a particular stage of development has been reached, no further development resulting from the influence of the surroundings is possible. A cell transplanted at an early age may develop in accordance with its new position, but at a later stage it will develop in accordance with its origin. In plants especially, the case is different. Specialized tissues and their cells, when cut off, can recover a plurality of potentialities even when the plant is fully grown. A single leaf of *Begonia* is capable of producing in every possible place tiny plants complete with root and stem.

[2] 1939, 1951.

It seems from this that there is a very serious discrepancy between the views of Driesch (1928) and the conclusions to be drawn from Spemann's (1936) experiments. Driesch established the plurality of potentialities in the germ cells. He claimed that an ideal whole, not immanent in the parts, aroused each of the latent potentialities so as to produce a complete organism on realization. We turned our attention to the parts termed germinal material, and treated this as though it were dough which just required kneading. But the germinal material, as we have tried to prove, is a mass of independent living beings. From this it follows that the metabiont is demonstrably a merogenous system in the first instance. The individual cell of a metabiont is homologous with the cell of a protist. Hence the metabiont is a sum or a colony of cells, each of which is an independent living thing. I hope I have proved that this is so.

3. THE MULTICELLULAR ORGANISM AS A UNIT

(a) *The Germ Cell and its Progeny*

The multicellular organism, then, is composed of as many living beings as it has cells. Let us now relate this statement to a number of important form problems.

That mother-cell or ovum, from which generations of cells take their origin, is itself a product of cell division. Where sexual reproduction occurs it is also the product of a fusion of cells. The same is true of a zygote, the product of the fusion of two sexual protist cells, for this, too, constitutes the mother-cell for numerous progeny. When many divisions have occurred a number, say n, cells have come from the mother cell, and these after dispersal live their separate lives in widely differing places.

Let us now assume that these n cells, instead of being scattered, live together in a community. In the case of protista such "crowding" is attended by a most unfavourable effect. The n cells of the same family injure one another by the products of their metabolism, if they are concentrated too closely. The social cell, however, definitely requires such crowding as a necessary condition of its environment. This is a new situation but it says no more than that the cell of a metabiont is socially disposed. The social juxtaposition gives rise to a social order of which the constituents express the laws governing the behaviour of the separate cells. The cell in the multicellular organism is structurally orientated in relation to its fellows, while the cell of the protist is made for independent living. The differing principles of multicellular and unicellular organization thus find their expression.

A second point which distinguishes the two types of cell is the heterogeneous nature of the offspring of a metabiont germ cell. If the descendants of a parent protist are maintained in identical conditions after a number of cell divisions, we can expect with certainty complete identity of appearance among them. The descendants of an ovum, on the other hand, very soon show signs of differentiation among the division products of the same stage. This is because, though of the same generation, they acquire very different forms and develop correspondingly into quite different organs. The comparison thus reveals that, given identical conditions, n cells of a protist coming from the same parent are alike after x divisions, while n cells of a metabiont after x divisions are quite unlike. I have already expressed the opinion that the difference may be due to exogenous factors, for the individual cells occupy different positions in the germ and thus occupy different environments. But these exogenous factors are not the only ones. Self-differentiation and the effect of external stimuli are others already mentioned. An argument often directed against Driesch is that cells develop in accordance with their "prospective significance" quite independently of other cells. Here one of their potentialities is realized in isolation. This proves that cells have predetermined tendencies; they have an urge to become something definite. They have, in addition, a tendency to influence their environment, and seem compelled to accept the rôle of an organizer of that environment. This tendency, too, is innate in the cell as an individual. As far as the stimulating cell is concerned, a development of endogenous origin is thus affected, and its cause is not outside itself; it is not entirely exogenous. Thus a new fact is established, a fact which is absent from the realm of unicellular organisms.

The divergence forced upon the *n* descendants of the ovum is not simply the result of exogenous stimulation; these cells have an endogenous and fruitful tendency to become different, quite independent of the position they occupy in the series of generations.

Now as regards this position in the generation series, we can be sure that it is of far less importance here than in the realm of the protista in determining the character of the cell. When two blastomeres are separated each produces a complete organism. According to Weismann (1892), the nucleus of the germ cell contains a mosaic of determinants which fix future characteristics. The whole complex of determinants, then, is found in the nucleus of the ovum and is the equivalent of the genotype. Every cell division separates the determinants farther and farther from one another, so that at every stage cells are produced which are poorer in determinants than the cells from which they take their origin. Finally each determinant is localized in a particular cell and finds its realization in that cell's characteristic form and composition. The genotype[3] has become the phenotype.[3]

This view virtually identifies the totality of the potentialities in the ovum with the genotype. The stored determinants would have to be fewer in number in any descendant of the ovum in proportion to the number of divisions which had taken place since division began. The stage of division would determine the number of determinants in the cell. Lillie gave precise expression to this idea in 1929 by using the term segregation for it. He claimed its validity for the ova of annelids, molluscs and tunicates. Cell division breaks up the ovum into segregates; when segregation is complete, each segregate is confined to a single cell. This is Weismann's view exactly; but Driesch's researches, which have given us the concept of pluripotency,

[3] Genotype—that which a thing *is* in its germplasm; phenotype—what a thing looks like.—Editor.

have already refuted it as regards the so-called "regulation ova". Lillie, however, does take Driesch's researches into account, for he accepts a double process for the regulation ova. This amounts to making a distinction between "regulation ova" and "mosaic ova". Lillie held that, in regulation ova, segregation does not occur at the same time as cleavage. What is more likely is that by division a number of equipotential cells are formed, in which the potentialities of the ovum are shared equally among a large number of cells. The blastomere, therefore, is in no sense connected with the function of the cells which will proceed from it. Segregation follows only later. At a certain stage of embryonic development cells with equal potentialities begin to divide into cells with different segregates.

What is meant by this segregation? Assuming we have a mass of cells with multiple potentialities, how are these potentialities realized, realized in such a way that a different potentiality is realized in each cell, and moreover so that each contributes to the formation of the whole? If, as far as the blastomeres are concerned, endogenous processes are at work, it is amazing that the realized potentialities fit together as a whole. It is surely more probable that the potentialities are aroused by something which is itself a whole. We thus return to Driesch's entelechy; only it makes its presence felt later, at the end of cleavage and the beginning of segregation. Of course, Lillie (1929) could hardly be supposed to hold a view of this sort.

Vogt (1923), too, accepted a double process of determination, though it is double in quite another way. He held that a "formation movement" or "dynamic determination" can be distinguished from the histological differentiation which represents a "material determination". It follows from all this that the divergence which produces separate cell individuals cannot be a differentiation due to cell division; the condition of the cell in the course of its embryonic development is not determined by division and the stage it has reached in the generation series. A little further consideration should convince us of this.

From egg to embryo a definite number of cell divisions

occur. At the two-cell stage each half is capable of giving rise to a complete organism. At this point each half-egg has one stage of division behind it. If, however, it can yield the same result as the whole undivided egg, the organism produced is one stage further on in the series of divisions than an organism produced by a whole egg. Further, if half a gastrula is able to produce a complete embryo, the organism which results is many divisions ahead of a normal embryo. These considerations seem conclusive; it cannot be the place in the series of generations, it cannot be the division, which induces or evokes this segregation or separation of the determinants.

We are now in a position to answer the third question we put in two ways.

The form of a metabiont is not exclusively the product of segregating cell divisions; new cell characteristics appear, but they are associated with no particular stage in the series of generations. "New" characteristics are simply those that are suddenly acquired by the cells of the germ and whose antecedents are as yet unrecognizable.

Now, after n cells have been formed following x mitoses of a protist cell, these n cells are completely uninfluenced by each other. Each cell leads its own independent life unless crowding occurs. The life of each cell runs its course as though no brother cells existed. On the division of the cell the two new masses of material are quite independent of one another. From one cell or one life two cells and two living entities have come into existence. If half of the n cells derived from a common protist ancestor were to die, their fate would be without the slightest effect on the remaining $n/2$ cells. But if $n/2$ blastomeres of the germ of a metabiont were to die, this would be a matter of crucial significance for the rest. The remaining $n/2$ blastomeres would either increase forthwith to n cells, or they would live on vegetatively for a while and then die. This latter effect would be the case if the process of determination had gone too far for the other alternative to be possible. The life of one cell is therefore causally dependent upon the life of the other cells. It would be misleading to explain this by saying that the biotope of the one cell was so altered by the disappearance or reduction of "crowding" that a new phase of existence was engendered in it. The following fact renders such an explanation impossible. The cells left behind do not replace those which are lost in a purely quantitative manner. The complete germ produced by the remainder is smaller in proportion to the mass lost. The cell mass which remains replaces the lost portion qualitatively. If the cell qualities are K, L, M and N, and M and N are removed, K and L divide in such a way that cell types K, L, M and N are once more present. The M and N potentialities in the K and L cells are realized as soon as M and N are no longer actually present. The space-form of the organism is by this means completed when each cellular element of the form is represented by one or more cells. If the form element is missing, cells appear to fill the breach; these are produced by those still available.

If this phenomenon is explained by correlation the following problem presents itself: If certain areas of the germ undertake the work of organizers and induce certain formations in other areas of the germ, the formation of certain organs must be suppressed when these organizing cells are removed. On the other hand, when the areas of passive reaction are removed, the remaining areas will have to be organized so as to form the missing organs. This does in fact seem to happen. In the case of the germ tissue of amphibia, if certain areas are removed, certain processes fail to occur; if, however, others areas are removed, regeneration replaces what has been lost. This is as it should be; it corresponds with the conclusions we have already reached. But why do the organizers organize only in the absence of whatever it is they can organize? Why is their activity at an end when everything has been organized? Why do they organize only to the extent that something is lacking? For example, they will not induce the formation of a whole axial system but only just the amount that is required in the particular case.

Induction is doubtless an active awakening of passive

10

potentialities. But where are these potentialities? The expected answer is "in the germinal material". But there is no such material, nothing in the nature of an organic plastic rubber. We have shown that there are merely living beings, cells: these constitute the germinal material. It is in cells, therefore, that potentialities are awakened to realities, and there are just so many potentialities as will enable the resultant realities to form a whole and no more. This principle may be seen at work even when foreign tissue is grafted, for the grafted material makes the other cells, its hosts, co-operate in the formation of the part which is missing. This fact teaches us that at any given time all the cells necessary to form the whole organism are produced, provided the active and passive potentialities are available.

Thus the ordering of the individual cell-life is dependent entirely upon the individual life of that cell. But in the metabiont there is a tendency to produce all the types of cell which "ought" to appear in the completed metabiont.

(b) *Purposiveness*

The order existing in a metabiont is a correlation of elements of different quality. We established earlier on that the stage reached in the process of cell division was without effect as regards differentiation. We also showed that the cells were mutually dependent and subject to the multicellular form. In just one of Boveri's (1905) experiments both facts make their appearance simultaneously. The experiment also enables us to prove that the sequence of the divisions is not without its dependence.

By shaking sea-urchin eggs, Boveri broke them up into fragments, some of which had nuclei while others had none. When these fragments were treated with spermal fluid, a sperm made its way into each fragment whether it had a nucleus or not. All these fragments developed. The sperm nucleus fused with the egg nucleus, where there was one, to form a normal diploid nucleus ready for cleavage. In egg fragments without nuclei the sperm nucleus remained solitary and was thus haploid. The diploid eggs had twice the number of chromosomes and twice as big a nucleus as the haploid ones. Both types of egg then proceeded to develop. Let us recall at this point what we said earlier of the nucleus-cytoplasm relationship: a larger quantity of cytoplasm goes with a larger nucleus, i.e. the larger the nucleus the larger the cell, for their sizes bear a definite relationship one to the other. This relationship is therefore a constant. Later stages in this experiment revealed a very instructive difference. In the case of the diploid gastrulae, nuclei and cells were twice as big as in the haploid gastrulae, but there were twice as many of the haploid cells. Here we have a pointer to all we wish to know. Since the cells are haploid, they can only achieve half normal size; yet they still form a gastrula. Since they must form a gastrula, they have to take twice as many steps in their process of division; they divide, therefore, twice as frequently as under normal conditions. They have to make up in number what they lack in size. It is a purpose, therefore, which forces them to divide as they do. The gastrula is a goal to be attained. To attain it, quite different unicellular partial processes are necessary in each case. If the process went on in the "normal" manner in the case of the haploid germs, gastrulation would become impossible. An abnormal procedure occurs to make a gastrula possible. In Boveri's (1905) experiment all the later stages are the same up to the pluteus larva. This experiment is analogous to Driesch's experiments with the division of embryos. One would expect that half an egg would produce half an animal, and think it impossible to develop an embryo from half an egg and from a haploid nucleus. The fact that a regular multicellular organism is so evolved is a proof that the cells—the material possibility—are urged to develop in a manner quite at variance with their original determination—their "prospective significance". The latter would amount to an endogenously determined, independent cell-development. We are now in a position to state our fourth conclusion:

The cell, along with its immanent potentialities, develops in the direction of a goal that cannot be explained by its nature, a goal which transcends the natural constitution of the individual cell. To express it quite baldly, the cells must develop one way or another, each way being absolutely different; yet in each case the goal remains constant. In an orchestral symphony nothing is present but musicians, their instruments and a conductor with his baton. But is the piece which the musicians perform with their conductor no more than a correlation of the actions of the participants? It is a correlation, of course, but the correlation, i.e. what the musicians are playing at any one moment, is determined by the score, which indicates to each participant what he has to do.

(c) *Space-form and Time-form of the Metabiont*

Every cell undergoes development from the moment it is born through the division of the mother cell until it ceases to exist owing to its own division. Both the division and the structure of the daughter cells depend upon potentialities which are realized by the life of the cell itself. The bases of these potentialities must be sought in the life-process of the cell. We have already shown that all the cells of a metabiont have an individual life of this sort. But is the life of a metabiont no more than the sum total of the lives of the cell-elements? If this were the case, the life of the metabiont would be something essentially composite; its time-form would be a sham and the laws of its nature could be resolved into the laws governing the individual cells which compose it. Here the distinction Gustav Wolff (1933) drew between a "cumulus" and an unordered heap comes to mind. Even a cumulus consisting of particles exhibits a form relationship.

In our particular instance the cumulus shows a polar differentiation; its particles are exposed to a secondary and therefore accidental determination—one which is independent of their inner character. This is due to the position they occupy at the summit or base of the cumulus, or at some intermediate point. Order is visible here, too, but it is a merogenous order, i.e. the elements themselves determine how the cumulus as an entity is formed and where every constituent element is to lie in it. If, then, there is no more here than a correlation, we can and indeed must recognize in the metabiont an all-embracing order; this order, however, is one which is clearly and exclusively determined by the parts.

On the other hand if a whole is at work here, the fate of the elements which compose it must be determined by the time-form. Some may doubt whether this distinction has any validity. We must, therefore, show that such a distinction is possible. For if it is possible to explain the whole as deriving from the time-form of its elements, the cell's element-determination can be established. But if the element, in its time-form, proves to be determined by the whole, and dependent upon the whole, if it belongs to the whole simply as a member, we should have to admit that the member can be recognized as such only by abstract reasoning; it cannot be objectively detached from the whole and shown to be an independent thing.

We have now to make up our minds whether the cell, in its time-form, is something independent or something related to a whole. For this reason I at first ignored the traditional discussion of the embryos of the sea-urchin or the salamander and made the cell of the protist my starting point.

Everything that has been said shows that purposiveness is immanent in the cell; that this purposiveness is caught up, so to speak, in a higher purpose in the metabiont; that, while the cell of the protist is free, the cell of the metabiont is in bondage. The laws governing the cell are all that rule in the protist; in the metabiont they are subservient. The successive stages in the form of the cell differ according to whether the cell is part of an organism or not. The members of cell generations acquire a very definite relationship: cells divide and change with a specific function in view, a function quite unconnected with the cell. The connection appears in the goal which is reached only after several generations. The interplay between the limitations of the cells and the purposiveness which transcends them is made clear by Boveri's (1905) experiments. To sum up then, the cell of a protist has its own natural structure, expressed in its "space-" and "time-forms" and leads a separate life in accordance with its nature. By its biotope or environment, it may acquire a new phase of existence and so receive secondary modification. An example is provided by the flagellate with its swarm-spore, palmella stage and cyst. The cell of the multicellular organism, however, acquires, besides its nature as a cell, a significance resulting from the rôle it plays, the place it occupies in the organism.

The experiments described above enable us to recognize the correlation of the separate cells as something induced. At the same time we can see how the purposive striving of distinct processes is concentrated. It is superfluous to remark how extraordinarily specialized the lens of the eye is. Its development is induced by the optic cup. Yet the whole of the ectoderm is capable of producing the lens. The fact that it is formed is the expression of a correlation. Hence the particular process consists in two tissues exerting an influence, the one upon the other. But the lens has a function only over the optic cup and it is the optic cup which induces the formation of the lens. These facts give a hologenous stamp of purposive striving to the merogenous correlation. The whole is the result of the unified purposiveness of the parts superimposed upon a merogenous interaction of those parts. We have already proved something similar in connection with chemical components. The single part is completely meaningless in isolation. The lens lacks sense without an eye, the spinal marrow without the supporting vertebrae. Thus the correlation, although operating automatically, becomes utterly meaningless once removed from the sphere of the whole. The life of the individual cell and the sequence of the links in the chain of the generations are inexplicable in terms of the nature of the separate cell. The phenomena connected with the individual cell can be understood only on the basis of their connection with the whole organism. The multicellular organism is accordingly a whole; it is governed by its own laws which create a system based on units of a cellular order.

(d) *Antagonism between Unicellular and Multicellular Order*

We should have a striking proof of the existence of two principles of wholeness one of which is superimposed upon the other, if we found an instance in which the two could be genuinely separated. The following examples should provide such a proof.

A sponge can be completely destroyed by having its soft body pressed through a pad of gauze. By this means the individual cells are almost completely isolated from one another. If we assume that the isolated cells possess some sort of biological cohesion—a tendency of the isolated cells to make contact with their fellows (a tendency which has never been proved to exist)—the most we could expect is that the isolated cells would unite. But if this completely disintegrated sponge is put into a glass dish, twenty-four hours later a completely normal sponge will be found, just as though nothing had happened. The individual cells which compose it are so constituted that they can once more restore the sponge in its original form. No doubt some re-differentiation of the individual cells takes place here so that they "change their jobs". Now, how does it come about that isolated cells contain within themselves the principle of order and harmony of the sponge body, with its choanocytes and its channels governing the ebb and flow of water, so that the various elements re-form the entire system, perfectly, and in all its complexity? Even if we could suppose that each cell possessed human intelligence, we could not explain this process as merogenous; the organization as a whole demands a degree of division of labour among many homogeneous cells, and this could not be expected of any individual cell. The cells arrange themselves all in due order. They differentiate themselves in such a way as to form an outer epithelium which leaves pores open between the cells, channels which lead to the whip-chambers, and other channels leading from them into a common vent or oscule. Besides this, the cells on the outside, the oscule cells, form a flat epithelium; the cells in the whip-chambers develop into the collar cells, etc. Between all these, stretches a gelatinous connective tissue in which meristematic amoeboid cells are to be found. These at first secrete calcareous material or silica needles, but, if an injury is sustained, they at once take the place of any cells which may be destroyed, assuming the cell-form required.

Thus we have here an astonishing example of an order making for wholeness which cannot be looked for in the separate cells. We can see plainly here the opponent of dis-order, the principle which restores order to the various parts when their order is upset, marshalling them once more so that they form a unit. The goal aimed at is the sponge-body, which operates simultaneously as a cause upon the cellular elements. Thus we have once more a typical example of goal-causality. It is not an embryo with which we are concerned here—a germ in the process of growth; it is a fully grown animal body, and there are numerous cells which are very loosely attached to one another, for the majority are separated by gelatinous matter. If we add that a single cell of *Cladophora*[4] can regenerate a complete plant, and a single arm of a starfish, a complete animal, we can expect to find in the cells the passive but not the active potentiality of the whole form. Examples in support of this thesis are very numerous.

It is obvious that we are dealing here with a good deal more than a segregation of potentialities. A botanical example will illustrate this. A single leaf of *Begonia* is far from being any-thing whole; the cells which lead to a new formation of root and stem, leaves and flowers, were long since determined as epidermal or even end-cells. Yet there slumbers within all of them the potentiality of developing all that the normal plant needs. But does a cell of this sort, which has received its determination, form a whole in somewhat the same way as the much more primitive *Cladophora*? Certainly not, for all those leaf-cells, which play their part in forming a whole, first divide into unspecialized embryonic cells. It is certain that all higher plants have meristematic cells of multiple potentiality; growing

4 An alga.

points show evidence of this universal potentiality in many ways; leaves, roots and everything possible develop from them. In our *Begonia* leaf, however, we have a case of entirely new formations which would never have occurred unless the connection with the parent plant had been broken. These specialized leaf-cells originated in divisions of an embryonic cell possessing a whole range of potentialities; they had received a determination for one special function—epidermal or end-cells. They would have continued in this function until the leaf faded. But when the leaf was severed, the cell, so determined, began to divide into cells of an embryonic meristematic character. Meristematic cells had the power of becoming epidermal cells, but the facts prove that epidermal cells can also revert to meristematic cells. If the secondary embryonic cell has universal potentiality, so has its parent the epidermis cell. We see here a reversible process; a determination already effective can be revoked. We must conclude, therefore, that when one potentiality is activated, the others are not extinguished.

It is often held that such a cell would be capable of forming any other sort of *Begonia* but that it is prevented from doing so by the presence of other cells. It was thus forced in a particular direction. But if the other cells are removed, this hindrance is also removed. The endogenous striving towards the development of multiple potentiality is freed. If this view were correct, a merogenous principle of growth would be at work here; there would be no more than a correlation between the individual cells. Another fact, however, will show that this is untrue, and will reveal the antagonism which can exist between the unicellular and the multicellular orders. Boysen-Jensen[5] the eminent plant physiologist, in his *Pflanzenphysiologie* stated that it is possible to take the cells from the callus tissue of a *Nicotiana* hybrid and to keep them alive as a tissue culture. Although the cells continue to divide, a plant with cell differentiation never results. The tissue remains an

[5] 1939, p. 333.

unordered mass of cells. This is a proof that the single cell is governed by its own laws, as previously affirmed, and as tissue cultures confirm. In this case there is no differentiation and no overriding principles of order. This shows that when new formations arise from a callus, some additional agent is at work, and that this stands in the way of the individual cells developing on their own initiative.

If, as a rule, all that prevents every cell developing every one of its potentialities is the presence of other cells, every callus cell would tend to become a complete plant. If secondary embryonic tissue is produced, as in the leaf of *Begonia*, in certain situations by the division of cells which have their specialized functions already fixed, a large number of such cells will form an unordered heap of cells like those of *Nicotiana* in the case mentioned. But order then comes to the heap; entirely new potentialities are awakened, but in such a way that the realization of particular ones forms an entity, a whole. Thus not every cell becomes a plant; instead, the heap of secondary embryonic cells, the descendants of a number of parent cells, develops into a new shoot and a new root, to which each cell makes its contribution. It is not one cell but the combination of all the cells which produces the new plant. Every cell has many potentialities; but it is an order governing the ultimate whole which determines which of these potentialities is to be realized. This order making for wholeness cannot be identified with the competition resulting from the growth of individual cells. If proof is needed of the genuine effectiveness of the morphogenetic factor of wholeness, as existing outside or above the cells, this proof is here. In the two extreme cases of the sponge and the *Begonia* it was brought dramatically to our notice. We saw it directly opposed to the unicellular order of things. It operates upon elements which have become disarranged, restoring them to order.

This wholeness factor is not only to be seen as the enemy of disorder and decay. It is at work wherever a new order is imposed upon an order already existing, as in the case of vegetative reproduction.

4. THE HIERARCHICAL ORDER OF THE ORGANIC FORM

J. von Uexküll (1920) made a distinction, applicable equally to the products of human art and living beings, between the material of which they are made and their forms. Thus a locomotive has the molecular structure of iron, but the form of a locomotive. The nature of the material is basic to the object made from it, for example the material for a knife must possess a certain degree of hardness and a persistent shape. Although this is so, the molecular structure of the material bears no theoretical or essential relationship to the finished form. The grain in the wood is irrelevant to the efficiency of a boat made from it. The living organism, too, has its material substructure, but, as Uexküll pointed out, it is completely irrelevant to the articulation of the living form. The material basis exists exclusively for the finished form.

"Finished form" in the abstract cannot exist; it is something imprinted upon material already in existence. An ordered form results only from the moulding of the material basis. Form and its material basis cannot be substituted for one another, or regarded as identical. The clay can receive a form but never create it.

Applying these ideas to matter as such, we find that it always has a structure. Differences in its structure determine the differences of the elements. The elementary structure, i.e. the structure of the atoms, is a basis for a superior structure, for it includes a tendency for saturation, a thirst so to speak, which leads it to form molecules. Now the cell is a finished form. The finished form of a living being is impressed upon the material substructure, unifying all the particles of matter. Expressed differently, the finished form, e.g. the cell, is based upon the matter composing it, but is neither implicit nor immanent in it. Bertalanffy (1949) was wrong in describing the origin of a living thing as a simple passage of its material elements to a higher level. What really happens is that these elements receive a form from outside. The form is not immanent in them. Hence it is also quite misleading of

Woltereck (1940), to describe the vital operative factor as "interior" and the matter upon which it operates as "exterior". The life factor is not concealed within the material substance of which the living being is formed. It comes as it were from outside and gives articulation to the material.

Hedwig Conrad-Martius (1944) believed that the entelechy extends its influence deep into the structure of matter and creates for itself as it were a matter of its own. Fundamentally this is correct for it can be proved empirically, but it cannot be pushed too far. Similarly Uexküll (1920) was of the opinion that, in a living organism, the material structure and the finished form correspond in every detail. Quite the opposite is the case with a tool made by human hands. Uexküll claimed that the structure of the living substance reveals nothing that is not directly connected to the articulation or organization of that same living substance. I agree with this, but I believe that the boundary line between the material substructure and the articulated form must be drawn rather differently.

I do not think that the intra-atomic structure of the assimilated food can be changed. The atoms inside and outside the organism are the same to begin with. This is true also of many compounds such as amino-acids, sugar or fatty acids, even when they are incorporated and stored as food in the organism. Otherwise we should be forced to believe that the laws of chemistry become inoperative inside the organism, and this is not so. The atomic forces corresponding to the atomic structure are the same inside and outside the organism. The novelty which is added is the controlled and regular manner in which the separate, structurally-conditioned chemical reactions take place. Under this sustained control, molecules are produced which, as we saw earlier in the book, could only arise under conditions which have to be deliberately imitated in the laboratory. For this reason it is my view that the organic molecule is even at this stage an example of articulation, for its structure of atoms has been built up by forces external to them. What we may regard as the "inorganic" characteristic of the organic molecule is its articulation. Apart from the above, I am in entire agreement with Uexküll[6] and Conrad-Martius.[7] Once an atom enters a molecule its unsatisfied electro-affinities are satisfied and it becomes subject to different laws. In scientific language it has become something else. In actual fact the carbon atom, when it co-operates to form a micell, is different from the elementary carbon atom. It is different again from the carbon atom which shares in the building of a molecule of carbon dioxide. The same applies, *mutatis mutandis*, to substances such as those of the amino-acids.

In the organism at work, molecules are expressly built from atoms into articulated forms, for they cannot arise outside the living system of the cell. The organic molecules can, therefore, be called the machines of the cell. The form-elements of the cell, such as the genom or the nucleus (if one thinks of it as separated), are similar machines. Uexküll (1920), too, was of the opinion that machines are constructed in the cell, but he holds that protoplasm has that vital form-constructing tendency which is the mark of life. Now it is my opinion that the whole of the protoplasm consists, from a material point of view, of a vast number of such machines, but that what may be called the "non-machine" is quite distinct and separate. It builds machines and collaborates with them, but it is not identical with them. The cell, therefore, is an order which directs matter deliberately along certain lines, so that the result is that unity, that whole, which we call the cell. For this reason the cell is not a whole in the same sense that a molecule is; it is consti-tuted on different principles.

The multicellular organism, however, works primarily with cells, not with molecules. Just as the cell's entelechy attacks and masters the molecules, so the metabiont's entelechy dominates the cell. There is furthermore, according to Huzella (1941) an intercellular organization. This consists of the form-elements of the multicellular organism. The cells, of course, were made to produce these, but they have become

[6] 1920.   [7] 1944.

emancipated, and, though still under the control of the body's entelechy, they are independent of the cells. The entelechy of the cell, like that of the metabiont, is no rigid form. It is something always in the course of happening; thus it gives to the cell its time-form. It is thus comparable with a sort of river which carries with it into the current of activity the material particles. The all-embracing entelechy, too, carries the activity of the separate cells into the activity of its own system, a system governed by laws, a system, too, which is both end-result and cause. Thus in a multicellular organism there are two entelechial systems at work. The cellular entelechy is responsible for the basic organic syntheses; the cell possesses the "formative entelechy". Thus, while we have but one entelechy in the protist, we have in the metabiont, besides the entelechies of the individual cells, the all-embracing entelechy of the organism as a whole.

In order to bring home even more impressively this surprising distinction between, and opposition of, two entelechies, I will describe a remarkable experiment performed by Spemann (1936). He transferred the primitive gut membrane of a frog to the mouth area of a salamander embryo. The graft developed in accordance with its situation; it became part of the mouth area. The entelechy of the organism had assigned this task to the graft. But the task was not given to the material as such, but to the cells—a fact which is evident from the way in which it was carried out. In the body of the salamander the gut membrane of a frog produced a mouth where a mouth ought to be—but it was a frog's mouth. The cells were frog cells; they could produce nothing but frog organs. This they did though in origin they were gut membrane cells. They did not follow the prospective tendencies of their original location, tendencies which were immanent in them. It follows, therefore, that they were subject to the influence of a superior form-principle. It is for this reason that they supplied mouth instead of gut membrane. But if the entelechy had issued its orders to molecules as Driesch's notions would suggest, a salamander's mouth would have resulted. The fact that a frog mouth was produced shows that the only prospective potentiality present was one of producing frog organs. Such prospective potentiality is to be looked for not in the molecules but in the cells. Somehow the command to produce mouth is received at this particular spot. The grafted cells obey this command as best they can, but they can only produce the mouth parts of a frog. Thus it appears that there are laws governing the cells as individuals; they cannot in this case be other than frog cells. This is proof of the fact that the cells have a life independent of the greater whole. On the other hand this individual operation of the cell was urged to a development quite out of accord with its origin. In this instance we have proof that the cell's individual life is subordinated to a higher purpose, that of the organism as a whole.

If we compare the various multicellular organisms we find that the connections between individual cells and the whole organism vary greatly in their degree of firmness. In sponge, alga and polyp the cells seem to function autonomously like those of protists. They seem to follow the organism's "master plan" only in their spatial arrangement and special form. In other cases, such as those of *Nematoda* or *Rotatoria*, the number of cells forming the body, or even each single organ, remains constant. Here the freedom of individual cells is limited to a very high degree. Thus the cells in organisms enjoy varying degrees of independent existence. Interstitial cells in sponges and *Cnidaria*, and leucocytes in the blood of vertebrates, lead almost the same sort of independent life as the protista. Cells located in a rigid tissue are subject to strict control.

It is my opinion that the cell of the protist corresponds in no way to a complete metabiont. It corresponds only to one of its cells. As independent organisms, protista and metabionts are on quite different planes. We are now confronted with the question of the relationship of the entelechy of the whole to the entelechies of the parts. We get the impression from what has been said above that the cells of a metabiont are like recruits to a regiment which are forced to accept a strict discipline, whereas protista are permitted to lead their own comfortable lives. This comparison suggests that in spite of similarities, there is a difference in principle between the two types of cell. When a protist divides into two cells, these have no further interest in one another and go their separate ways. We defined entelechy as a system of laws operating in a definite field. Once the field has divided, two independent law-systems hold sway; this means that with the two cells the entelechy of the parent cell divides too. But since the division of the cell is due to the activity of the entelechy, we shall have to go so far as to say that, since the entelechy of the parent cell divided, the division into two daughter cells was the inevitable result. The entelechy accordingly ceases to exist, but it lives on, in a sense, as do the two derivative cells, in its two daughter entelechies.

The ovum, too, divides uninterruptedly into a number of individual cells. Yet it is possible to prove empirically that these individual cells are subject to a unified control. As the ovum does not contain all the cells of the organism to be, but divides to bring these into existence, we cannot assume the existence in the ovum of all the entelechies of the cells which are to come later. The ovum divides in response to its own laws. These laws, immanent in it, express its life principle, its entelechy. On its division into two cells, two cell-entelechies arise and the multiplication of entelechies continues. Yet in spite of all the division, something remains undivided and continues as a whole. The individual cells become members of a whole. Thus division of the entelechies is a deployment rather than a division comparable to that of protista.

In my use of the word "entelechy" I am anxious not to be misunderstood. I was very hesitant about using it, because it has so many associations. Yet I was unwilling to add to the vast number of technical terms already in use. My task in this book is simply to give an empirical basis to ideas. Every term is intended to express something really objective. My entelechy has nothing to do with any ontological Platonic "idea". In the field of the cell an order has been seen to exist, and this order must of necessity be described as teleological, one in which the goal or end is included in the cause. The goal aimed at by the order is a whole. Nevertheless, the factor which gives to the constituent matter this transcendent end-causality can be sought only in the cell and in the organism, where we have in fact found it. By abstraction I can grasp the harmony or identity reigning among individuals of the same species, but this does not entitle me to assume that my idea existed as substantial form before the thing itself. It is only on the basis of such harmony or identity that I arrive at the conclusion: nature shows me nothing but harmony; hence I can only express the harmony existing among the individuals of a species by re-discovering this same order in each separate individual. But it does not follow that because the order coincides, the being under observation is the same. In the field of living things I have had experience of something I choose to call "entelechy" and I limit the use of the term to this field. I am therefore obliged to assume the existence of as many cell-entelechies as there are cells, and as many whole-entelechies as there are metabionts. The order expressed by the entelechy is by no means the same as the entelechy itself. In respect to the matter it directs, the entelechy is transcendent; in regard to the organism it dominates, it is immanent. It is the order governing things that I regard as transcendent; but this order can be seen in the individuals only in their conformity.

Let us sum up our conclusions on the form-problem as follows:

The form of the cell is a principle which operates and is immanent in the cell. It is not identical with the substances to be found in the cell and not immanent in them. We call this *forma corporis* of the cell its entelechy, and say that it operates not on a *materia prima* but on a *materia signata* already made up of atoms and molecules: the entelechy changes this *materia signata* to a certain degree and in a decisive manner.

In the metabiont, too, an immaterial teleological principle is at work. We call this the general entelechy of the metabiont. This entelechy operates neither upon *materia prima* nor

11

materia signata but upon cells, already alive, and finally upon their products exterior to the cells.

We end this chapter with two short conclusions:

1. The form of the cell produces the cell from inanimate matter.

2. The *forma corporis* of the metabiont produces the metabiont from cells.

VI

ADAPTATION AND REACTIVITY

1. THE CAUSAL ORDER

A STONE in a landscape is determined by the qualities inherent in it—by its chemical composition, size, weight and form. It is given character also by the position it occupies in space. The factors of its environment are not without influence upon it. The shade from a near-by tree may prevent it from being heated by the sun's rays. In all important ways, however, the stone will remain uninfluenced by its surroundings. It is true that geology shows that it is a product of external forces in the past. At the moment, however, it is in a state of equilibrium and this is sufficiently stable to resist external influences. It could, of course, be brought into a different state of equilibrium, if some potential were developed between the mass of the stone and its environment. What then occurs is nothing more than a neutralization of this potential which leads to some change in the structure of the stone.

Much the same could be said of a beetle living under the stone. The beetle is what it is by reason of its own structure and form and by reason of its relationship with the things which surround it. It exhibits a stability which shows it to be a product of the process of development postulated by the theory of evolution. But one thing marks it off clearly from the stone; its stability is the outward expression of an instability in its chemical structure. Moreover, it is a matter of complete indifference to a stone if it is broken by another stone. When it is smashed, the fragments continue to exist just as though they were still connected. This shows that the momentary structure and the momentary form of the stone are only very superficially connected. The structure it is which makes the stone essentially what it is. Its momentary form determines it only accidentally.

But the beetle is characterized essentially by its independent existence. Further, the detached leg of a beetle will always be explicable only as a part of a whole beetle; the beetle's form, that is to say, determines the beetle's nature and its substance. What we need to study now is the causal relationship between the beetle and its environment, both animate and inanimate. This has been touched upon already in our discussion of the distinction between exogenously and endogenously caused morphological variations.

It is certainly quite wrong and quite unjustifiable to regard the processes of metabolism and morphogenesis as spontaneous manifestations of life, while the effects of stimulation are regarded as essentially different and as manifestations of life with exogenous causes. Metabolism consists in an exchange between what is external and what is internal. The same applies to morphogenesis, which cannot dispense with a series of external factors. Besides, the reactivity of the organism has its roots in the innermost being of a metabiont. Without doubt, the organism owes the harmonious working together of all its parts to the circumstance that the working of one organ influences another, i.e. one organ exerts a stimulus upon another, which is geared to respond with an effect. Thus the parts of the whole march in step together owing to a causal relationship between them. These processes are often purely endogenous and are quite unrelated to external stimuli. Irritability has been defined as those changes which are linked with changes in the environment, but this we shall have to reject from the start. All the same, we are forced to study these facts primarily in those phenomena in which a causal factor is certain. In practice such a factor is a simple external one.

This fundamental position is no less important in regard to the other great problems of dynamics and form. Yet in these the danger of wandering off the track is smaller. We were considering the organism's reactivity. Although chemical physiology and developmental physiology make use of experiments, the observer always remains outside what he is judging.

Any subjective attitude to the objects he is studying is foreign to him.

In the physiology of stimuli two difficulties arise at this point. The observer makes one essential condition himself, and then endeavours to draw conclusions from the observations consequent upon the conditions he has made. A pre-arranged and thus adequately known potentiality gives rise to a certain actuality, itself known to some extent—the action and change. What are the unknown potentialities which were realized on the way between stimulation and response? An alternative is then suggested, the two extreme forms of which would lead to unforeseeable results. Changes are meant which are also called "actions" especially where the higher animals are concerned. And why not? There is no objection to this in itself. The organs which are the proper receptors of this stimulation are like the corresponding organ of my own body. The stimulation is effective both for me and the experimental animal. The animal behaves just as I would under the influence of the same stimulation. Thus we may say that when the animal acts, it acts from the same motive as I do. Further consequences follow from this. A *Paramecium*, for example, consisting of a single ciliated cell, resembles me in several respects. It is sensitive to the earth, electrical stimuli and touch; I go to lectures and concerts. Animals, it is said, experience love and hate, feel uncomfortable and long for things just as human beings do. Thus they are just another sort of "human being". This kind of "anthropopsychologism" is common in the literature of animal psychology. All conclusions based on such ideas are open to very serious doubt; as knowledge they are worthless. Such reasoning is the Scylla of the physiology of stimuli and animal psychology. I would call it "egomorphism".

The corresponding Charybdis avoids all such prejudices and regards the living thing as something quite unrelated to humanity, as something whose relations with other things are as fortuitous as those of stones in a sack. Things "happen to coincide" and all we have to do is to confirm this fact and go no further. In both cases mistaken principles and prejudice are at work, and these make results built on such foundations mere fairy tales.

It is important to make clear that all the factors which are questionable—the object of the experiment and the factor whose effect upon this object I want to investigate—are contained in the consciousness of the investigator. Both are made known to me by stimuli proceeding from them. If I want to find out how an object affects an animal, I concentrate on one quality of the object, such as its colour, and notice whether this colour is perceived by the animal under investigation. How can I establish the fact which I am after—namely whether the object really is taken note of by the animal? I can only do so, if I can myself perceive a definite alteration in the object of my research when it is faced with one of these definite qualities of which I am aware. In other words it is questionable whether one content of perception conforms with another content of perception, whether a definite change in the living organism under observation is regularly linked up with a stimulus of which I am aware.

Thus a certain "behaviour" is the fundamental phenomenon studied alike by the physiology of stimuli and animal psychology. The most I can do, then, is to establish a certain concurrence or linkage of the stimulus with a definite piece of behaviour on the part of the animal studied. Assuming that the animal exhibits the same defensive movements in response to very different stimuli, I can never be sure that these different stimuli are felt differently by the animal or not. To pronounce on this matter, I must find out what it is in my stimulating object which causes the animal to behave in that way. I shall, therefore, have to isolate as far as possible all the qualities I perceive in the object and then find out if the behaviour is correlated with only one of these factors. This procedure, known as "factor-analysis", is the fundamental pre-requisite for all successful research in the realms of the physiology of stimulation and animal psychology.

Facts established in this way would, of course, be little more than the recorded results of experiments. In the course of time a mass of such exact facts would be gathered, but they would not be connected in any intelligible manner. Positivists, in fact, would limit the scope of biology to recording such facts. But even a police report on a road accident looks for some cause; we are seeking the springs of behaviour in the object of our experiments.

The following viewpoint also needs consideration. If I observe the effect of free nitric acid upon a living creature, this fact is very interesting, but, by itself, it is almost meaningless and without value. It can be understood as a chemical process but never as a biological one. Everyone will now inquire; since free nitric acid never comes into contact with living matter except in experiments, is not there something about the nitric acid, e.g. its ion-concentration, which corresponds with something which does in fact exist in the animal's environment? Is there no regular connection between certain observable chemical and physical phenomena and the occurrence of life? The branch of science which deals with problems of this sort is ecology. It is never possible to discuss the occurrence of any living creature at a given point in nature without relating its fundamental organization, its *morphe*, to its environment. Thus we see that many spheres of investigation which result in the accumulation of mere facts are all necessary. Only when their findings are reviewed together is a synthesis possible. The synthesis enables us to put forward a causal explanation.

A particular mode of behaviour fits in with, or is regularly associated with, the operation of some external factor, and peculiarities of form are regularly linked with certain details of the environment. We first establish a regular concurrence of the form with the environment, or show that the one results from the other; a *cum hoc* or a *post hoc* is thus proven. We have then to find out the connection between the two; we seek the *propter hoc*.

2. ECOLOGICAL ADAPTATION

Returning to our example of the beetle living under the

stone, we soon notice that this is the normal habitat of the beetles of this species. We soon find that we can assign a definite type of environment to every living creature. In that environment it will always be found. Experience of this sort will enable us to say where in any particular area we should look for a certain animal or plant. Anybody reasonably familiar with aquatic biology will be able to say, almost at the first glance, what sorts of creatures are likely to be found in a particular pond, and what sorts are unlikely to be found there. By means of a soil test a plant physiologist can tell what sort of plant could do well in a particular spot. The fact that such pronouncements are possible is proof enough that there is a certain regularity in these matters. Once we can base our knowledge on the assurance which the experience of regularity brings, we can also establish scientific principles.

A fish, to take an example, is regularly found in water, but not only this—it is always found in a particular sort of water. Now if we define the whole environment in which a living creature occurs as its biotope, it appears that every particular species occurs in a biotope peculiar to itself, and that creature and biotope are definitely related. But if we tabulate these facts and expect the table to express our experience of regularity, we shall be bitterly disappointed. The living organism is not related to its biotope as members are to a body. There are, rather, certain definite constituents of a particular biotope which are necessary to a particular living creature. For example, the forest songster, *Phyloscopus sibillatrix*, is commonly found in beech woods. Elsewhere, however, one single beech tree sometimes suffices to keep it in the area. With our experience of regularity we can say, therefore, that the beech is a necessary condition for the occurrence of the bird. This conclusion is all the more striking in view of the fact that the bird is exclusively insectivorous. Thus both insects and the food the insects require are further necessary constituents of this bird's biotope. Then there is the much simpler case of a caterpillar which is always found upon the plant on which it feeds. Is this food plant by itself all that is needed for the occurrence of the caterpillar? Certainly not, for the creature also needs a definite temperature and a good many more things besides the food plant if it is to live. An analytical study of the environmental factors is necessary if we are to account for the occurrence of any particular species. Such an analysis divides the various elements into two classes—absolutely essential requirements and unessential concomitants. Two other birds, the redstart and the swift, will serve as concrete examples of this. We find both in quite lonely rocky districts and in towns. Both nest in rocky cliffs and eat flies. Both are attracted by human civilization, for the buildings of towns replace the rocky cliffs and, thanks to the arrangements of human civilization, there are plenty of flies available for food. We see, then, that cliffs and flies are indispensable for both birds. The bird, however, is not adapted to the biotope, but rather to certain factors of the biotope. Similarly the rubble of a railway embankment provides with a good substitute the flora which grow among loose stones. It is clear then that only a limited number of factors in its environment are essential for the creature within it.

The living organism, then, is adapted to its environment. If, therefore, a definite biotope, such as a pond or a forest, contains an abundance of living things, the environment of each inhabitant is different, since each species makes different demands upon the common biotope.

Let us now concentrate upon an isolated element in the environment, the temperature, for example. We can then compare the degrees of dependence upon it manifested by the various members of a biotope. We shall at once find a further notable divergence. One species can live only within very narrow temperature limits; others can tolerate a wide range of temperatures. The first type is said to be "stenothermal", the second "eurythermal". Similar facts can be established in regard to all environmental factors. Many plants are very fastidious about the chemistry of the soil in which they live, and many insects demand a special food-plant. Others are not so particular. We can distinguish these types by the terms "stenophagous" and "euryphagous". The extent of the claim made upon the environment by a species is called its "ecological valency". There are species which have a very limited ecological valency in one respect, and a considerable one in another. In spite of this, the demands upon its environment made by a species may be summarized in general terms like "stenoecious" and "euryecious".

Up to this point we have concentrated our attention upon the necessary environment for the living creature, which we have tended to portray as passively moulded by it. But the living organism is active too; it influences its environment. This other aspect of ecology was at one time called "etiology" and treated as a branch of morphology. In order, therefore, to discover the relation of a living being to its environment, we must also enquire into the rôle it plays in the environment. Although many creatures inhabit the same biotope, the way in which this happens is very characteristic for each species. In any one biotope, no two species live in exactly the same way. The biotope offers a number of possible ways of living which are open to a living creature. These possibilities are in fact utilized, so that in the circumstances given, entirely different creatures live in the same way in different parts of the earth. On the one hand, no two species lead the same type of life in the same biotope; on the other, distinct species in different parts of the world lead similar lives in their biotope. Dahl and Kühnelt[1] have given their attention to these facts, of which a striking example follows.

A frog, if not too large and provided it has the apparatus for holding on, can live as a tree-frog upon the leaves and bark of trees. "Tree-frog" is not merely the name of a particular species; it implies also a definite mode of existence. Kühnelt named the mode of life that a particular organism can lead in a particular biotope as its "life-form" (*Lebensform*). The "tree-frog" existence is a case in point. Throughout the New World and in a great part of the Old, a tree-frog existence is led by

[1] 1943–50.

genuine Tree-frogs, the Hylidae, which are akin to the toads. But the Hylidae are not to be found in India or Malaya. Yet all the requirements for a tree-frog existence are to be found there. It is, therefore, extremely significant that this opportunity does not remain unused. Here it is the Ranidae, relatives of the true water-frogs, which live as tree-frogs; they have toes adapted for adhering to leaves, and yet they are unrelated to the Tree-frogs properly so-called.

Areas of opportunity for forms of life such as these are comparable with building plots. In one country a plot will be occupied by one type of creature, in another by a different type. It is possible to find plenty of other instances of this. Asclepiadaceae and Euphorbiaceae, for example, may assume the qualities and behaviour of cacti.

Let us now examine the biotope from the point of view of the living creature. On analysing the organism's qualities, capacities and organs, we find them all related in some definite way to the outside world. Leaves with chloroplasts are adapted to light and serve to promote photosynthesis; fins are adapted to water and facilitate movement. Even if we have the creature before us preserved in spirit, we cannot explain it unless we can grasp its relation to its environment. It is usual to say that the organs of a living creature have a "task" and that they "subserve" this task. What do people really mean by this? These words are usually used thoughtlessly, but, in consideration of Kühnelt's "plots", they are not without meaning. The environment offers certain possibilities; for instance, water has its dissolved free oxygen, its specific gravity and its resistance to friction. Now the lower crustaceans, living in the water, store organic substances. If the chitinous covering of these crustaceans is crushed, these substances flow out. In contact with a suitable enzyme, they break up into molecules so small that they will pass through a semi-permeable membrane. Another side of the picture is presented by the fish. This organism requires free oxygen and organic substances for food. The water supplies the one and the crustaceans the other. The fish's gills are adapted to extract the oxygen, and its digestive tract to incorporate the materials from the crustaceans. Furthermore, the fish has special mechanisms to enable it to move about in the water and a swim-bladder relates the animal to the water's specific gravity. Thus the fish is perfectly adapted to its environment. We see, then, that there exists a harmony and correlation between the individual life and its environment. My reasons for putting ecology first among the topics discussed in this section are obvious: in ecology we have something to see, something that can be proved, whereas all our other conclusions must be reached by way of abstraction.

If, then, we talk of demands that are met, or problems that are solved in some particular way, we simply mean that there is a link-up or co-ordination of the qualities of the organism with the factors of its environment. The environment represents one potentiality. The counter-potentiality opposed to it is represented by the organs and the structure of the creature using it. The life lived in such circumstances is a reality resting upon both potentialities.

The question which now follows may strike any non-biologist as a joke, but it reveals the root problem of the evolution theory. The fish is commonly said to be adapted to the water. Could not one say just as truly that the water is adapted to the fish? The fish's life in the water is a reality, while water and fish-organism represent potentialities. But both are co-ordinated in so many ways that we must seek the principle which brought about this co-ordination. Adaptation implies a process which brings it about. We can agree, to begin with, that water can exist without fishes, but not fishes without water. People long ago inferred from this that fishes were produced from the water. A later idea, that of Lamarck, was that the water fashioned fishes from living things that were not yet fishes. Here we have an organism on the one side and its environment on the other: the environment brings about a change—a "phylogenetic regulation"—in the organism. The result is the adaptation of the organism to its environment. The outside world stimulates this regulative process, which results in the organism's adapting itself to its environment. If the environment changes, it induces corresponding changes in the living creatures. The changes, therefore, are always purposive: the process of accommodation moves towards an intended conclusion based upon the living creature's capacity for adapting itself. The environment shapes the organism; the organism fits in with it. According to Lamarck,[2] every living thing has this tendency towards purposive adaptation; but it is the environment which initiates change.

The mutation theory finds the initial factor of change in the organism itself. The mutant is a "new" variety of a species already existing and is in consequence the product of a vital process. Now mutation occurs quite regardless of the fact that its product, the mutant, does or does not fit into an environment. The mutant comes into existence independently of any influence coming from the biotope. Only when the mutant is complete is the question decided as to whether it can continue to exist and pass on its newly-acquired characteristics to its offspring. The causes of the change lie in the germplasm. Lamarck agreed on this point but he thought that the new formation needed an outside stimulus before it became actual. Thus we see neither theory fulfils the demands made upon it.

Taken by itself Lamarckism might well succeed in making intelligible the co-ordination between the living being and its environment. But, apart from the fact that the inheritance of acquired characteristics has never been conclusively proved, Lamarckism is encumbered with a quite uncritical presupposition. If the capacity for purposive adaptation is inherent in an organism, and if the offspring inherits the adaptation won by the parent, this adaptation must be capable of further intensification. Two possibilities now become apparent: (a) the organism inherits along with each adaptation a capacity for intensifying it, or (b) the parent which acquired the adaptation must have possessed, potentially, the capacity to intensify it, even though such an intensification would only become actual

[2] Lamarck, 1809, trans. Elliott, 1914.

in a following generation. This alternative is more in accord with the germplasm theory. If (b) is true, every living organism must already possess, potentially, all those responses or adaptations which any conceivable environmental factor could ever call forth. In this case, the potentiality of the giraffe's long neck would have to be sought, not in the giraffe's immediate forebear, but among the primitive flagellata. The latter would have to possess the potentialities of every possible adaptation that might be required by any living creature, anywhere, to fit into any conceivable environment. But this would be absurd. And so is Weismann's germplasm theory, for all Darwin's "individual variations" and all their possibilities of intensification would have to be contained in the earliest protista (or maybe in the inanimate matter from which they came).

Mutations, on the other hand, certainly occur and may be produced experimentally. Nevertheless the question of potentiality arises here, too. A species must contain potentially all the mutations which can arise from its genom.[3] If this is admitted, the flagellata received a "mutation ladder" to both the Compositae and the birds of paradise. Compared with Lamarckism, the mutation theory is at a great disadvantage when it comes to explaining adaptation. The mutation of one gene could scarcely lead to the production of a new species, capable of maintaining itself.[4] Any character arising as a result of mutation must be accompanied by the mutations of other genes, so that the functional equilibrium demanded by life may be attained.[4] It is usually held that, while most mutations are deleterious, occasionally, among the large number of offspring, one occurs fortuitously in which the mutated gene, or genes, are in complete harmony with all the other genes, and so the mutated organism can live. Much of the theory of this, however, is based upon experiments with the fruit fly, *Drosophila melanogaster,* which produces large numbers of offspring. The theory may not be applicable in cases where only a few

[3] In the sense that the genom must be initially capable of change in such a way as to produce the mutation.—Editor.

[4] The truth of these statements is doubtful.—Editor.

offspring are produced, as in the hoofed animals, etc.[5] However, even in these, mutations occur which are perpetuated, and genetically a recessive mutation can lie dormant in a population for a long time until it accumulates sufficiently to express itself. For further information the reader is referred to Timofeeff-Ressovsky.[6]

The adaptation of the organism to its environment has long been a feature of great importance in evolutionary theory and yet the ecology of organisms has presented many difficult problems to the evolutionist. Hence in modern times, ecology has played an increasingly important part in relation to the study of genetic evolutionary mechanisms. As long ago as 1920 Uexküll insisted that an explanation of the relations of the living organism to its surroundings, a study of its adaptation to its environment, was necessary to any understanding of the organism.

By adaptation here we understand, first and foremost, the active and passive relationship of the organism to its environment. As such, adaptation is a concrete and observable fact, and we should base all our theorizing upon it. Driesch (1928) understood by adaptation no more than an individual adaptation, and drew a distinction between primary and secondary adaptations. I cannot agree with him in this. Adaptation is recognizable as of the very nature of the living organism. It is the presupposition for all the individual accommodations it makes, as we shall attempt to show later.

I propose to call the "relatedness" of the living being in its basic form, the fitting of the species into its environment, *fundamental adaptation*. All that Driesch called adaptation, I regard as *individual adaptations* which are secondary to the fundamental adaptations, though they must have their bases in it.

[5] In this paragraph the author in one sense overstates the problem and in another sense understates it. This fault is probably due to an excessive oversimplification and the conclusions he comes to are thus vitiated. Some of his statements are not really valid, and few, if any, geneticists would agree with his views on mutations.—Editor.

[6] 1937, 1940.

3. FORM AS THE EXPRESSION OF ADAPTATION

If we compare all the relationships which have been established in the cases of individual species, a certain regularity soon becomes obvious. Breathing organs always possess delicate membranes through which gases easily diffuse, and a surface which is as extensive as possible. Parasites engender a vast progeny in enormous genital organs, which increases the probability of infection. The organs of locomotion, in particular, manifest their typical peculiarities of relation to environment. The regularity of the co-ordination is so far-reaching that the knowledge of an organ enables us to infer its function and, with this, its environment. R. Hesse[7] and O. Abel (1912), working independently, were able to formulate laws of co-ordination on this basis. Wherever we find certain morphological peculiarities, we find also certain corresponding environmental features. Wherever, in land vertebrates, we find a reduction in the size of the phalanges of hand or foot, accompanied by a tendency to form a single axis, simultaneously with the loss of the collar bone, we have before us a swift-running animal. On the other hand, wherever we find a strengthening or even a multiplication of the digits and a strongly developed collar bone, we have a digging or scratching animal. If then we find a saurian with kangaroo-like legs we can reasonably infer that it leaps like a kangaroo. The function of legs like those of grasshoppers, frogs, hares and kangaroos is made abundantly clear by the lever movement of the joints; a use for these joints other than jumping is out of the question. Thus conclusions made from the study of fossil footprints are justified. In the case of *Compsognatus*, both the leaping legs and the impressions made by the animal when sitting, walking and jumping have been found in the earth, so that there can be no doubt concerning the animal's method of locomotion. Hence if we find such extremities we can assume the leaping habits of the animal with all the certainty which our experience of regularity affords us.

[7] 1935, 1943.

Every single ability, every single morphological adaptation requires, however, a considerable number of additional arrangements; an extremity of a peculiar type requires the appropriate muscles; a special apparatus for sprinkling insects with pollen involves a complete flowering mechanism with this end in view. An adaptation can never be an isolated phenomenon; the co-ordination of a whole complex of organs is always involved. One organ is adapted to the outside world, while the other organs are adapted to *it*.

The remarkable similarities among plants or animals which live in much the same way are known as "convergence phenomena". Similarities of biotope and the manner of living in it give rise to multiple adaptations. The result of these is a number of far-reaching likenesses. Certain well-defined ecological types arise which are often represented by creatures of widely differing structural groups. The ecological type of the succulent plant is strikingly represented by the cactus. Now the Asclepiadaceae and the Euphorbiaceae, in a similar environment, can give rise to succulents of the same type, which, in certain regions, completely oust the cacti. The torpedo or shuttle form which characterizes certain fishes is not confined to fishes. It may be found in no less than three mammals quite unconnected with one another, namely, whales, seals and sea-cows.

The stone of which we spoke at the beginning of this chapter was a product of its prehistory. The relationship of the living organism with its environment is constant and therefore regulated by laws. The organism lives both in and by its environment. The fact that the same biotope contains an immense variety of living forms, indicates that the same environment can be utilized and exploited in very different ways. A study of the purpose of a living organism leads us to a functional analysis of that organism; a study of the purpose of a stone, on the other hands, leads nowhere. Thus we can see that we are dealing with something real, an ordered relationship, when we regard the environmental connections of an

12

organism as "fundamental adaptation". This can be summed up by saying simply that a stone has a past but no future.

4. THE PHYSIOLOGY OF STIMULATION

The living thing does not exist merely for itself; its form is also the expression of its belonging to a definite living community. This is what we have called its fundamental adaptation. By this we mean simply that the environment and the creature fit in with one another.

But the environment to which the organism is so conspicuously adapted is constantly changing. It is a particularly impressive fact that the living creature, too, changes with the environment, and always, as we shall see, in a complementary manner. When a lifeless molecule is influenced by its environment and changes, this change is a rearrangement; the atoms of two molecules reacting with one another build up molecules which were not present before the reaction; they are its product. The living organism changes, too, to correspond with its environment, but its change amounts to a maintenance of the life process. It adapts itself to the needs of the moment in order—to remain what it was before. Apart from this, the living organism influences its environment and to some extent forms it. The living thing, therefore, is capable of *acting*. And since any such action is co-ordinated with a change in the environment and is therefore a response to a change in that environment, we can call it a reaction. Once more we find a regularity in the way in which the living organism reacts to anything coming from outside itself. "Adaptation" refers to the fundamental organization of the living creature—that organization which is basically its own through its fitting into its environment. "Reaction" expresses the ability of the organism to be moved itself to alter by changes in the environment. Everything that comes from outside is called stimulus. The change manifested by the living creature in response to the stimulus is the "reaction". Let us consider in more detail the precise meanings of these terms.

In an experiment the stimulus is something provided by the

experimenter. The experimenter brings to bear upon the object of his experiment a factor known by himself. He tries to find out whether this factor, his "thing", is a real thing to the object of his experiment. The only means he has of telling whether his "thing" is felt as real by the object is a visible or appreciable reaction. It may be, of course, that the living creature on its side can perceive things that the observer cannot. Things may well exist which are present to the animal observed, but which are not things at all in the consciousness of the observer. This is a difficulty, in any case, which cannot be easily overcome. It would be presumptuous on the part of the observer to conclude from his observations: "All those things which are things to me, and cause a reaction in the object of my experiment, are also things to it, and have existence for it." It is not legitimate to assume that all the things from which stimuli proceed are real things from the point of view of the creature we are studying. This is the error of the "egomorphist"; it sets reaction and stimulus one against the other, regarding the separation between them as something real. In the physiology of stimulation, the stimulus becomes a stimulus through the reaction it provokes; the reaction is a reaction purely on account of the stimulus which causes it. The observer can learn of the one only through the other. Both are phases of a single objective sequence and can be separated only arbitrarily. The considerations that follow will indicate what actually takes place when we perceive something.

We can perform the most varied operations upon a living creature, and find perhaps that the reaction to all of them is the same. Can we then conclude from this that the things which are so different for me are identical for the object of the experiment? On the other hand, things which for me are identical may provoke quite different reactions. Are these things, identical to me, as different to the object of the experiment as the reactions are different from one another? It is one of the great contributions of the physiology of stimuli to have recognized that the thing which I see as one thing, falls apart into a whole mass of elements when analysed further. The observer himself is the first to recognize this. The method consists in separating these elements, which I recognize, separating them, as it were, from the thing itself, and then allowing them to operate upon the experimental object, the reactions of which are carefully observed. At once differences appear in the mode of reaction. These differences are co-ordinated with definite elements. The concept of stimulation can thus be even more restricted. It becomes clear from such experiments that what for us is a "thing" is a whole complex of factors capable of provoking reactions, and that it is these, and not the thing as such, which issue the stimuli. We recognize things by their characteristics. Similarly the object of our experiments would seem to recognize certain characteristics to which it reacts. By these it "knows" the thing. We must accordingly break the "things" up in accordance with their characteristics. This becomes even more obvious when one thing is exchanged for another. One and the same characteristic shared by two different things, e.g. a colour or a distinctive outline, produces identical reactions in animals. We can say, therefore, that one or several characteristics are the stimulating factors, that these for the organism are the real things, while the object possessing them is unessential.

The stimulus, then, is that state of affairs, that situation, that fact, through which the reaction is brought about; it is that external factor which is the regular condition for the reaction.

The stimulative process, then, is the inference from the connection we make between the cause of the stimulus and the reaction. It is, therefore, a state with an outside cause. I have for this reason to call the outside factor the *cause* of the stimulus but not the stimulus or stimulus-element itself.

It is not the thing as such that produces a stimulus but some characteristic perceived by us, e.g. some chemical or optical emission; it is this which stimulates the organism, putting it into that state which becomes manifest to the observer in a later stage, the reaction. If, therefore, we speak of light stimuli we mean this: The light as such is no stimulus, but if a certain reaction is linked to it, we conclude that the light can set in motion a process in the body of the object with which we are experimenting. Light becomes important as a stimulating factor only when the effect of the stimulus is observable in the reaction.

These facts make us want to discover what exactly the state of stimulation is. We get near to answering this if the following question is asked: What precisely is the subject of this stimulation as a result of this external influence? Is it the whole organism? In the unicellular order, among the protista this seems to be the case, although the existence of light-sensitive spots might lead us to believe that parts of the cell are more sensitive than others. The multicellular organisms, however, possess organs which are obviously intended to receive special influences. The stimulus must first be received. Either the whole body or a part specially provided for this purpose changes in response to the stimulating cause. These special organs are known as organs of perception. If they are removed or damaged, the reaction fails to occur. The relation of the organ of perception to the stimulus is seen in the behaviour of the organs for the maintenance of equilibrium. Here the change in the organ on the reception of the stimulus can be observed. We can prevent the reception of the stimulus simply by removing a statolith from the organ. The change is then prevented. The eye, too, provides an easy means of observing the effects of stimuli upon an organ of perception.

The receptive organ, then, is influenced by, and alters in correspondence with, certain external situations. It is definitely related to the external factors. The eye is related to optical factors, the ear to acoustic factors, smell and taste to chemical factors and the statoliths to position in space. Of course, the reaction is the only measure of perception. There is still one link missing in the chain of proof before we can agree upon a final definition of stimulus. At one end we have the sense organ, at the other we have some phenomenon, such as a movement, which regularly follows upon a stimulation of the sense organ. The sense organ is, therefore, twofold: perceptive or receptive organ, and organ of response or result, in which we observe the effect of the stimulation.

The state produced in the organ of perception by the operation of the outside factor itself produces a certain state in the organ of response. Both states are co-ordinated. This brings us a good deal nearer to explaining the nature of the reaction phenomenon. A stimulus is a definite kind of change, caused by some external factor which is brought about in the organ of perception; it is, besides, that which is transferred to the organ of response. Therefore the stimulus must as such be conducted further. The means by which it is conducted varies from organism to organism, as we shall see. That it is so conducted, however, is something which can be proved. The stimulus can be traced right from the point of its reception to the point at which the result appears. Simple animals and all plants possess organs of both perception and response. There are also specific organs for conducting the stimulus. These may take the form of mobile substances which travel from the perceptor to the organ of response, or, as in the higher animals, they may constitute a nervous system.

We are now in a position to give a universally valid explanation of a stimulus. A definite condition of the medium—light, sound vibrations, chemicals or mechanical contact—evokes a change in the organ of perception. The changed state in the organ causes a change of the protoplasm, a liquid or a nerve, and this change, in its turn, produces a change in the organ of response. The stimulated state of the organ of response shows itself externally, e.g. as the contraction of a muscle or the secretion of a gland. One change thus follows another. One physico-chemical change initiates another physico-chemical change. Thus there is a serial co-ordination of physico-chemical reactions, though this could not be comprehended as a series, if the actions were seen separately. Each separate process is a physical or chemical one; viewed as a whole, the process is not explicable in terms of order or co-ordination, since it is a forward movement in which each step becomes significant as a result of its connection with the other steps, and in respect of the goal to which it leads. Seen in isolation, the separate step or stage would appear meaningless. This serial connection of the stages is pre-stabilized by the nature of the organ of perception, the factors conducting the stimulus and the organs of response. Hence we can define stimulus as that process which is based upon the linkage determined or pre-stabilized by the initial organization.

There remain now the actions which occur spontaneously—without being excited by an external factor. The response organs appear to function without any "orders" from an organ of perception. The actions, however, can be proved to be provoked. The difference lies in the fact that the stimulation comes from inside the organism. The phenomenon of stimulation here is essentially the same as in the previous cases. The stimulus comes from an endogenous factor. This factor can be removed and, when it is, the reaction fails to occur. It is also possible to block the connection between the endogenous stimulating factor and the organ of response; once again the reaction is prevented. It is possible, furthermore, to substitute a corresponding exogenous factor for the endogenous one. In this case the reaction occurs as usual. An endocrine gland is such an endogenous factor. If it is removed from the body, and doses of the hormone which it secretes are administered, the same reactions are produced. That such a reaction is of the same nature as the others, will be shown later.

The reverse process is also possible; an exogenous factor can produce endogenous consequences, but the reactions of these are not manifested externally. I can satisfy myself that they take place only by dissecting the animal involved. All these facts lead us to the conclusion that the whole organism can be analysed into reaction systems, and we become finally aware that processes amounting to reactions are also taking place purely endogenously. All systems of organs, all the cells even, are mutually influencing one another through stimuli which take longer or shorter routes. If a process ensues purely endogenously, one organ in a particular state becomes the cause of corresponding states in other organs. This agrees

exactly with our definition of a reaction; a sense organ is also
an organ of the body, and its condition when subjected to
stimulus determines the degree of stimulation in the processes
it initiates. The sole difference lies in the fact that in the case
of the sense organ an external factor produces the stimulating
condition. Thus the life of an organism consists of reaction
processes going on side by side and in conjunction with one
another.

Physiology is in a position to go further than this. The
stimulus which arises from hormone activity, in particular,
creates a causal chain of separate physico-chemical processes.
As a result of the stimulus, or train of excitation, all the organs
or cells involved form a unity. The stimulus, whether caused
endogenously or exogenously, is awaited by an organization
which is able to gather all the minute separate processes into a
unity. The stimulus is not fortuitous; it is expected. The organism's power of being stimulated precedes the actual stimulus.
We call the system of an organism which links all possible
causes with all the possible effects, appropriate to its kind, its
reaction system.

5. THE BIOLOGICAL RELEVANCE OF PHYSIOLOGICAL STIMULI

I have undertaken to relate the fundamental adaptation of
the form to its natural surroundings with the facts of stimulation physiology. The task is rather surprising because these
two aspects of life are quite distinct and seem to be unrelated.
Adaptation is concerned with form, and response to stimuli
with behaviour. Yet there is something which unites them.
Both are concerned with the organism's relationship with the
world outside itself. In one case a species occurs regularly in a
definite ecological sphere to which its form is suitably adapted.
This implies that each species grows, swims or flies in its
biotope. Has growth anything in common with swimming or
flying? The theory of evolution undertook to explain this and
to show the connection. Zoology was, as Abel (1912) said, in
danger of becoming a science concerned only with specimens
preserved in spirits. Living things simply must be studied in

conjunction with their environment if they are to be understood. Uexküll[8] did a great service to biology in bringing together physiological behaviour and ecological discoveries.

The connection between ecological adaptation and response to stimuli in everyday behaviour is not easily shown. The difficulty derives from the fact that reactions originate in so many different ways. A common explanation for these varied happenings has often been offered. One rule of behaviour is accepted as the only genuine one. Anything that does not fit in is regarded then as a deviation. Thus Pavlov[9] and his school regarded reflex action as the standard type of reaction, and tried to make all the facts fit into this norm. Other people ascribe a kind of consciousness to the plant "soul". Henri Bergson (1907) desired to ascribe consciousness to every natural object capable of movement. Things that could not move he regarded as being rather "dull". To him life is movement, but this movement is a permanent, creative flow of happenings, which, strictly speaking, can be apprehended only intuitively. Thus everything must have consciousness to some extent. Bierens de Haan (1940) held a different view. He was not seeking to generalize. He wanted to reduce things to order. His teaching was founded on the very just recognition of the fact that there is a broad correspondence in the way animals behave, and that these ways of behaviour may be distinguished from one another according to their degree of rigidity or plasticity. When, earlier on, we spoke of nothing but a reaction, we meant essentially the same thing as Bierens de Haan. The only difference between his view and ours is that we reject any kind of anthropomorphism and regard instinct as a special case, a definite norm of reaction.

We shall be justified in bringing under one heading the various types of reaction only after describing each norm separately. Let us first look at a few examples of adaptation.

If dandelion seeds are sown in two different places, one shady and the other sunny, we shall obtain plants with big leaves in the shady place and plants with small leaves in the

[8] 1920, 1921.   [9] 1926, 1932. Engl. Trans. by V. Andrep, 1927.

sunny place. When the light is scanty, a bigger absorbing surface is required than when the light is intense, if the same
amount of light energy is necessary for photosynthesis. The
leaf size is related to these requirements. In recent years it has
been discovered that in certain flowering plants the development of the flowers depends upon the length of the day. Some
plants will not develop flowers at all until the day reaches a
certain length. On the other hand, plants that flower in spring
blossom only when the light is of relatively short duration.
Plants which in other respects are active from spring to autumn
nevertheless blossom at quite different times of the year. In
both cases we have examples of the adaptation of the form
to a definite external situation. This adaptation is not innate
as such; it is inborn in the individual as a potentiality. Similarly
the same species sometimes has the power to reproduce itself
both sexually and parthenogenetically. The way chosen is
determined by external factors. Among the crustaceae, the
Chladozeres produce females only, parthenogenetically, in
favourable conditions. In unfavourable conditions, as in winter
or when the water in which they live dries up, males are first
produced; and the females produce a very different type of egg
which requires to be fertilized. The males accomplish this.
The same female which has repeatedly produced females parthenogenetically in favourable circumstances, can, still parthenogenetically, bring forth males or eggs needing fertilization.
These are once more adaptations, but, in contrast to our
"fundamental adaptations", they modify a course of life
already determined.

All these are cases of adaptation which depend upon the
activation of various potential capacities existing side by side;
first one and then the other is brought to its development by
external circumstances. Such facts lead on the one side directly
to exogenously-conditioned morphogenetic processes, but on
the other, they represent a direct transition to those phenomena
called "reactions" in the physiology of stimuli.

If, then, we are to characterize a living creature according
to its capacity for adaptation, we have (a) the fundamental

adaptation, the form which corresponds basically to the ecological conditions, (b) the form's ability to change which is coordinated in a different way with changes in the environment. This capacity of the forms for change can be separated into primary or secondary adaptation. If the change is normal—one regularly related to a factor in the environment—the adaptation is primary. If the environmental factor upsets the usual function of the organism, so that it has to take steps to restore order, the adaptation is secondary. An adaptation which results from a change in the seasons gives rise to a new species. Another persists over a long time and is eventually irreversible. Another changes from month to month or even from week to week. All of them are in principle the same. Once we can accept this, the organism's capacity for reaction is a phenomenon precisely similar to adaptation.

I hope I have justified my discussion of adaptation on the same basis as the phenomena of stimulation.

Fishes, we saw, are morphologically related to the water. Their fins, swim-bladder and digestive systems are only effective if used at the right time in the right element. Now physiology pure and simple is concerned only with the mechanisms of the bladder, digestive system, etc. But these mechanisms become intelligible only when related to ecological factors.

Physiology shows us that the capacity for reaction rests upon a vast number of physico-chemical processes and a wide variety of morphological factors. It shows us furthermore that stimuli involve the existence, side by side, and intermingled in many ways, of a number of separate processes. A certain harmony seems to reign in the organism. Is this apparent harmony within the form, and in its adaptation to its environment, something real, or does it exist only in the mind of the experimenter? Let me indicate the point at issue in regard to morphology and ecology.

Shuttle-shaped "fish"—real fishes, whales and seals—are constructed for swift swimming. But the physiologist, dealing with stimuli, would have nothing to say about this, unless he were also an ecologist. Again, sound operates upon organs of perception; as a stimulus it is conducted along nerve tracks to the centre of the nervous system. Then, by means of other nerves, it sets going a reaction in some muscle or other. This is as far as the physiologist can go. No purpose can be deduced from this process if it is considered in isolation. A number of such processes are at work in the living creature, some dependent upon one another, others independent. If there is in fact some connection between them all, its significance is beyond the competence of the physiologist.

VII

NORMS OF REACTION

1. PROTOPLASMIC REACTIONS

ALL the functions performed by living organisms are exhibited by the simple cell. The functioning of the cell is presupposed by every living reaction system. It is cells which secrete the hormones; it is cells, too, which respond to the stimulation of hormones. Of course, the reactions exhibited by the protista are only protoplasmic reactions. The protoplasmic reaction is, then, primary in the physiology of stimuli. Many reactions indeed are limited to certain definite groups of living things, but no bodily reaction is conceivable without cellular action. But beyond the cells we cannot go, for if we break up their structure we come to molecules which do not exhibit physiological phenomena. We can, however, study the workings of the protoplasm, which has a colloidal structure. We do not as yet know how and why the protoplasm reacts, but certain details of it are open to study. The effects of a protoplasmic reaction can be seen.

It appears that the reception of a stimulus is limited to certain parts of the protoplasm; these parts at least are chiefly concerned with it. On the other hand, however, the cell responds in a very definite manner to stimuli which affect the whole body. We find in the protista, just as in the multicellular organisms, a sensitivity to particular stimulations, and these evoke fitting responses. Nevertheless, a large number of, to us, quite different external factors evoke from an organism the same response. For instance, the Slipper Animalcule, *Paramecium*, exhibits "fear" reactions when confronted with a number of particular but different situations. We can see the effects but it is impossible to say what goes on in the protoplasm.

Uexküll (1920) saw protoplasmic reaction as a reaction of a

special type which he called *Formhandlung*, "form action".
Its characteristics are the following: In a metaboint every
stimulus ends up in an organ producing appropriate effects or
actions. The excitation runs its course in accordance with a
rule already laid down in the creature's make-up. In the protist
we find nothing of the kind. Here we find a peculiarly plastic
capacity for producing spontaneously whatever the occasion
demands. Protozoa possess no digestive organs. But as soon as
food is digested, a vacuole is formed expressly to serve as a
stomach. Once its work is done it is re-absorbed. An amoeba
has no organs of locomotion. If, however, it is incited to move
by a stimulus, a pseudopodium is formed from any part of the
protoplasm. Once its task is performed it is withdrawn once
more into the rest. Uexküll regarded the protoplasm as the
primary plastic substance, really living material devoid of
machinery. All the tiny organs produced by the cell, such as
muscle and nerve fibres, may be regarded as machines constructed by the protoplasm. These may be purely transitory
formations like the pseudopodia or the vacuoles, or they may
be flagella, cilia, myofibrillae, etc., which are permanent
mechanisms. Once they are formed they continue to operate
and to react. The protoplasm interferes only when some repair
has to be done. The sarcoplasm of the muscle cell is the un-
constructed part, the non-machine. It is the part of the muscle
which is truly alive; the fibrillae are its machines. The unique
characteristic of the protoplasmic reaction is the plasticity of
the effector.

If we were to push Uexküll's view to its logical conclusion,
we should have to make a distinction between an organism's
living protoplasm and the machinery it has constructed. We
should then be confronted by a sort of biological dualism in the
reaction system. One could also assume, of course only by way
of hypothesis, that in the protoplasmic reaction a very complicated process of correlation takes place between hormonal
reactions. The tiny fungus *Pilobolus crystallinus*, which belongs
to the Mucoraceae, is distinctly phototropic, just as are the
higher plants. But it is not the whole mycelium but simply the

sporangiophore that bends and shoots out its sporangia towards the light. Its whole body consists, however, of nothing but a coenocytic mass of protoplasm from which the sporangium proper is divided by a septum. In the phototropic reaction there is doubtless no more than a purely protoplasmic reaction; this finds expression in a stronger growth of the cell-wall turned away from the light. Carotin, too, is found in the otherwise colourless fungus. Such resemblances suggest that this phototropism is a physiological process similar to the phototropism of the more highly organized plants. If this is so, then it, too, consists of a hormonal reaction. This in turn suggests that all protoplasmic reactions are hormonal. The process might then be envisaged as follows. Either an external or an internal factor occasions a chemical change in the protoplasm, and this alters the condition of the whole cell. In this condition, response actions occur which are co-ordinated with the initial stimulation. Further, the cell shows different degrees of response to reactions in different phases, which phases may be caused either endogenously or exogenously. For example only the haploid gametes, those especially equipped for the purpose, have a tendency to copulation; the material from which they are formed, on the other hand, is never capable of any such action.

However, in every case, the reaction is related to the stimulating factor in one of two ways: either the reaction integrates the factor with the life process to the advantage of the organism, or it excludes it because it is harmful. If, therefore, the protoplasmic reaction should turn out to be a physico-chemical phenomenon, we should know more about the co-ordinating principle which is characteristic of all reactions. We should then know that those happenings, which are known to occur in a complicated muticellular organism, occur also in simple protoplasm.

2. HORMONAL REACTIONS

In the tropisms of the higher plants a reaction occurs which Giersberg (1922) called "humoral". This term applies also to reactions brought about by hormones commonly called hormonal reactions.

Plants reveal phototropic and geotropic tendencies which result in their shoots growing towards the light and their roots away from the light and towards the earth. Normally the two factors at work cannot be distinguished from one another in all orthotropic plants, plants, that is, whose long axis is orientated along the line of the earth's radius: the light operates from above, the geotropism from below. All the same, quite a long time ago, it was proved that here two quite separate factors are in operation, each providing a stimulus for the plants. When, for example, a mustard seedling grown in water has light striking it from the side, the sprout turns towards the light and the root curls away from it. The shoot is positively, the root negatively, phototropic.

With regard to the other type of stimulus, Knight, in 1806, succeeded in showing that the mass of the earth and the pull of gravity affect the direction of growth. This he did by means of the following experiment: If one fastens germinating bean seeds to the rim of a wheel which is rotated vertically, the roots grow inwards from the point of view of the pulling force, that is, towards the centre; the shoots grow outwards away from the centre. In these conditions, the effect of light is completely cut out; the phototropic response is neutralized and is replaced by a pull of another sort. Moreover, there is another way of showing that the centrifugal force works like gravity. If the seeds are fixed on a wheel rotating horizontally, and the speed of revolution is regulated in such a way that the centrifugal force is equal to gravity, then the roots grow downwards and outwards at an angle of 45°, and the shoots grow upwards and inwards at an angle of 45°, to the radius of the wheel. Evidently two stimuli of the same type have joined to produce a pull on the principle of the parallelogram of forces: the two pulls are to be regarded as stimuli of precisely identical quality. This experiment proves that gravity by itself gives rise to geotropism quite independently of light.

Thus the direction of growth of a plant is determined chiefly by the two factors, light and gravity. Other tropisms may also play a part in plant growth, for example, hydrotropism, chemotropism or haptotropism in climbing plants. It may be added that growth in a transverse direction can be shown to exist in lateral roots and in branches of shoots. The growth is then at an angle to the line of the stimulus, gravity or light, that is, they are plagiotropic, and this is a behaviour which is advantageous to the plant from the standpoint of (a) photosynthesis in the case of branches and (b) the uptake of water and mineral salts in the case of lateral roots.

When a plant bends towards the light, the process of growth is determined in a definite direction: the side turned away from the light must necessarily grow quicker than that facing the light. It is now possible to prove that these differential growth rates are produced by a substance known as auxin. Auxin may be a compound of two substances, namely, Auxin A—$C_{18}H_{32}O_5$, and Auxin B—$C_{18}H_{30}O_4$. A third substance isolated from urine called heteroauxin was found to be an already well-known substance called β-indolylacetic acid (IAA). β-indolylacetic acid is probably the natural auxin present in higher plants. There is no evidence that auxins A and B are normally present. The effects of auxin are important to our arguments and hence a somewhat detailed description is given.

In the auxin experiments on plants the classical organ used is the oat coleoptile which is a protective sheath enveloping the shoot apex and young leaves of the oat seedling. Auxins formed in the extreme tip flow down in normal circumstances from the growing point equally all round and cause the plant to grow straight upwards, regularly. Now if the plant receives light from only one side, then either there is a transfer of auxin from the brighter side to the darker side, or else auxin on the brighter side is made inactive. In either case the result is the same—an increased amount of auxin is found on the shaded side. If, after the light has shone upon it, the tip of the coleoptile is cut off, and put upon a small plate of gelatinous agar, and if this plate of agar is next placed upon the coleoptile stump, there follows exactly the same bending as occurred

13

when the tip was present. This bending would not have taken place if the stump alone had been left. Thus the agar takes the place of the coleoptile tip, and it can do so because it has absorbed auxin. This experiment shows that the bending of the coleoptile is produced by auxin. We must now show that there is more auxin in the shaded side than in the brighter side of the coleoptile. For this the small agar plate which had been set upon the remains of the coleoptile is cut into two with a razor blade in such a way that one half absorbs the substance coming from the brighter side, and the other half the substance coming from the shaded side. The agar containing auxin from the shaded side produces much greater curvature than the piece coming from the light side. Careful measurements have shown that two-thirds of all the auxin produced by the coleoptile tip are on the shaded side, and only one-third upon the brighter side. The conclusion is that the substance auxin is the cause of all phototropic bending in higher plants. Thus the process of conducting the stimulus of light is found to be no more nor less than the equal or unequal distribution of auxin as it flows through the organism. Rays of light with long waves, i.e. red light, are relatively ineffective and the largest effect is associated with green, blue and violet waves. We may note here that two pigments, the carotinoids and the flavoproteins, have high absorptions in the blue region of the spectrum and may be involved in the phototropic response. It is noticeable that the positively phototropic fungus *Pilobolus* contains carotinoids, though it is otherwise colourless.

Nothing further is known of the process in detail. It is assumed that the blue-violet and yellow-green rays cause some unstable substance to break up, and auxin is made inactive by the products of its breaking up. Some such process will probably emerge from the enquiry: if this proves to be the case we will have before us some perfectly simple chemical reactions.

It would appear from these experiments that however many purely chemical processes are involved, in the long run it is the cell, the protoplasm, which is affected by the hormone auxin, so that growth in length occurs. But I am not prepared to halt my "mechanistic" explanations at this point. We may not as yet be able to explain the effects of auxin upon cytoplasm and nucleus, but I think we may take it that some such simple hormonal reactions occur in them, too. Similar processes must be going on in stalks and the flat surfaces of leaves which are similarly phototropic. But how are we to explain the remarkable co-ordination of all these processes? We are familiar with a change from positive to negative phototropism, and we can presume that similar simple processes are at the basis of these reactions. But how does it come about that a change of this sort occurs in just the way that is going most to benefit the plant? The compass plant *Lactuca scariola* turns the surface of its leaves towards the weak light of the morning and evening hours. In the hours of greatest illumination it turns the edges of its leaves to the sun. The flower stalks of *Linaria cymbalaria* are positively phototropic, so long as they are bearing flowers; they present the flowers to insect visitors. But when the fruits are being formed, the stalks become negatively phototropic, which results in this climbing plant pushing its fruits into the masonry of the wall on which it is growing. Each separate partial process is brought about by a simple chemical reaction, which is quite unrelated to the final general effect; yet the final effect is due to a co-ordination of all these processes. What each is incapable of achieving for itself is achieved by all together. Looked at in this way, the "phytohormone" auxin, simple as it is, is responsible for both phototropism and geotropism.

The distribution of auxin in the plant is determined by the earth's gravity. It flows in greater abundance on that side of stalks and roots which is turned towards the earth's centre. Experiments have proved that such an increase in auxin retards growth in roots and accelerates growth in shoots. It is evidently influenced by both the light of the sun and gravitation. Remarkable to relate, it produces opposite effects in root and stem. Yet the explanation is simple. It has been shown that 1 part of auxin in 50,000,000,000 produces quite a marked effect. If its concentration is increased, growth is restricted. It has been found that cells vary in their sensitivity to auxin. The same concentration promotes growth in one cell and restricts it in another. The cells of roots are markedly more responsive to the presence of auxin than shoot-cells. A like increase of auxin on the underside of a plant, laid down horizontally, promotes growth in the stem and restricts it in the root. The underside of the stem and the upper side of the root grow. Hence, under the influence of gravity, the shoot bends upwards and grows away from the earth, while the root bends downwards and grows into it. Simple and mechanical as it is in detail, the process is full of meaning and purpose when seen as a whole.

In order to make these remarkable processes somewhat clearer, I will say a little more about the origin and fate of auxin. We saw that in the oat coleoptile it was formed only at the apex of the stem. It is a secretion of the cells found there. It circulates in the plant in the normal way of liquids. The degree to which cells react to it varies considerably. It is a typical hormone; it issues from one set of cells and produces its effect in others. The weakness of its concentration suggests that its effects are catalytic; it would not be possible for so small a number of molecules to produce such extensive changes, if they formed a part of the final product.

As a hormone—a chemical messenger—auxin corresponds exactly with the hormones we find in animals. Note that auxin is not the chemical molecule as such; it is the molecule functioning as a connector of two cellular processes. It is this which makes it a hormone. When the primary sex organs of vertebrates have reached a certain stage of development, they too send out hormonal messengers which cause growth in certain cells prepared for this purpose; the result is the development of secondary sexual characteristics. The special character of auxin lies in the fact that gravitation and light affect its movements, i.e. its distribution throughout the plant. Of course, light and gravity are external factors, while primary and secondary sex organs are internal or external bodily organs. But this makes no real difference. When the growth hormone (somatotrophin), secreted by the anterior lobe of the vertebrate hypohysis (the complete pituitary gland), is inhibited by the sex hormone, or where, on the contrary, the adrenocorticotrophic hormone (corticotrophin), from the anterior lobe of the hypohysis, influences the activity of the adrenal cortex, we see that the effect of a hormone can be modified after its emission, or its emission can be affected. The fact that the effects of hormones can be influenced by external factors is clear from the winter sleep of cold-blooded animals; during this period of rest the emission of thyroxin from the thyroid is suspended. This process is precisely similar to that connected with auxin. By means of a chemical process, cells secrete a substance which has a catalytic effect on other cells. Looked at physiologically, we have here a perfectly simple correlation of different processes; but biologically these processes are quite specifically co-ordinated. All these processes are effective within a definite order; they are "tuned-in" to one another, as are the separate instruments of an orchestra by the score. The organ of response, those cells in which the effect of the hormone becomes manifest, is "waiting" for the hormone like a lock for its key. The "waiting" amounts to a potentiality which is realized by the operation of the hormone.

These analogies may be questioned. We cannot really think that, for instance, hydrogen peroxide is waiting for manganese dioxide and platinum in order to explode. The relation between these substances originates in the experience of the scientist. This is true of hydrogen peroxide and manganese dioxide, but in the sphere of life we should remember the distinction we made between the physiological and the biological approach. To a pure physiologist each separate occurrence is no more than a catalytic process. In inanimate nature such processes go on all over the place without any connection. But in the sphere of life it is we who have imported the process of analysis—a procedure quite foreign to natural processes. We have arbitrarily broken up into separate processes a phenomenon which is in fact a whole. The course taken by individual processes, however, is no more objective than the co-ordination of these separate processes. In the sphere of inanimate things it is the experimenter who produces this relationship by arranging the separate processes in succession to one another. In the realm of living things, however, what is subjective and arbitrary is the splitting up of the whole process. If we break up a chain of reactions into a number of sections, arbitrarily fixed by ourselves, we must not forget that the fragments we have picked out from the total process once formed a single whole. The analogy of the chain, which is so useful, is not really appropriate. The reaction is far better compared to a thread which we methodically cut into bits, the length of which is also fixed arbitrarily by us. If we want to know what the thread is, we must not forget that it was originally a single piece. The task of science cannot be completed by separation and analysis; the analysis must be followed by a synthesis.

3. REFLEX ACTIONS

The characteristic of the reaction called "reflex" is the "reflex arc". An organ specially constructed to receive certain stimuli is excited by the external stimulating factor. The organ possesses sensitive cells which seem to be "waiting" for the particular stimulus for which they are made, so that they may change as it changes. It is usual to call this change "excitation" but it must be understood that such a state of excitation may be constant. The statolithic organ of an aquatic animal, and the eye by day, are examples of receptive organs which are in a state of constant excitation.

If a sense organ and its nerves are in a state of constant excitation, this fact can only be known to us by sensible changes in it. We can perceive these, for instance, if we remove the factor causing them. This does not imply that the excitation is expressed only in actions; continuing excitation is possible without a following reaction. But, since for the experimenter excitation can be recognized only by reaction, action is in practice demanded as a criterion. Mention is frequently made of excitation but this can be used appropriately only when speaking of organs of reflex action. It would be difficult to apply the term to the action of hormones.

The important thing about a reflex action is not only the special organ of perception but also its means of transmission; the specific stimulus is carried along a special path and evokes a specific response. Thus the change in the sense organ produces a changed condition of the connecting nerve, and this finally produces, as the effect of the stimulus, a definite change in the acting organ. The activity thus provoked may be the contraction of a muscle cell or a secretion from a gland cell. These three—the reception of the stimulus, the path along which the excitation travels and the final result—form the "reflex arc". This is a morphological fixture.

In reflex action the stimulus received by the appropriate organ is conducted from cell to cell until it reaches the organ which "reacts". Hormone reaction is more diffuse. In reflex action, the path taken by the stimulus has no turnings. To any specific stimulus there can be but one response. This is the standard pattern of reflex action, though it is sometimes complicated. Any phenomena which do not conform to this type should not be called reflex.

It is the reflex arc which is absent from hormone reactions. The reflex and hormone systems are outwardly the same, in that there is stimulation and response in both cases. Effects such as phototropism can be produced in some cases by reflex as well as hormonal action. In different animals the same effect may be produced, in one case by reflex, in the other by hormone action. Both shrimps and fishes can accommodate themselves to the colours of their environment. In both cases the receptive organ is the eye. In both cases the organs of response are the pigment cells of the skin. Yet in the shrimp the means of linkage is a hormone, while in the fish it is a nervous system.

The reflex arc can be demonstrated experimentally, for it is possible to dissect out a nerve and the muscle to which it belongs, and observe the functioning of the two together *in vitro*.

Considerations such as these led to the theory of paths and centres, a theory which has received support from the fact that the mode of transmission in the nerve can be shown in many cases to be electrical. Many have regarded this process as the basic phenomenon of the physiology of stimuli. The reflex, in the sense in which I have defined it, however, can only be a special case which cannot be generalized. However, even when applied only to reflex action, the theory of paths and centres is riddled with difficulties. The system of telegraphs is used popularly as an analogy. The telegram handed into the apparatus (the organ of perception) is conducted along a wire (the centripetal nerve) to the telegraph office (the central nervous system); thence it finally reaches the addressee (the organ of response).

But it has been proved that reflex connections are in general amenable in so high a degree to regulation, that they can hardly correspond to simple telegraph wires. They can scarcely be thought of as such, even if it is assumed that they make many connections between the organs to which they are required to conduct stimuli. Lorenz (1937) justly pointed to the "wiping reflex" of the frog: the animal, from which the brain has been removed, will lift right or left leg to wipe off an irritant from its flank. Thus the path theory is very misleading. It confuses the model with the original thing.

I should like to oppose this mechanistic exaggeration with a vitalistic one. I have already pointed to the danger of using expressions like "perceiving" and "taking notice" in respect of reflex actions. I have occasion now to repeat my warning. These expressions and their implications are quite irrelevant to reflexes and to other phenomena studied by the physiology of stimulation. It is never possible to be certain that an animal notices anything. All one can be sure about is that it reacts. It is possible to follow the path back from the reaction to the stimulus, and to see their relationship. If the stimulus provokes no reaction we cannot conclude that the animal has not "noticed" it, even if we can prove that a "stream of action" or some "wave motion" has occurred in the sense organ. The observable reaction as the normal consequence of nerve processes is the sole criterion we have that a stimulus has been received. To speak of "perceiving" in such a connection does violence to words.

Accordingly a reflex must be defined as a connection, made by nerves or at least cells, between the organ of perception and that of response; along this line of linkage runs the reflex arc. Reflex action is automatic, and is modifiable only to the extent that the reflex is subject to a certain degree of control.

4. INSTINCTIVE ACTIONS

In the last section we saw that the difference between reflex and hormone reactions consisted in the different methods used to transmit the stimuli. Instinctive action appears to be a much more complicated process. The organs for maintaining equilibrium are co-ordinated with movements of swimming or crawling by reflexes. On the other hand the care of the young, patterns of courtship, the treatment of prey or of enemies, all of which involve extremely complicated behaviour, are said to be instinctive. Instinct here appears to be a potentiality for carrying out these stereotyped patterns of behaviour. It does not seem difficult to distinguish instinctive from plastic actions.[1] Hence, disagreeing here with Lloyd Morgan,[2] Spencer,[3] Alverdes[4] and Bierens de Haan,[5] I propose to limit the term "instinctive" to actions which conform to the following specifications:

1. Instinctive actions are peculiar to the species and can be performed equally well by all the members of the species.

2. Instinctive actions do not vary. They give the impression of being automatic, for they are performed as though under compulsion. They resemble a cinema film which remains the same however many times it is shown.

[1] Lorenz, 1931; 1937a, b; 1939; 1943.
[2] 1912.   [3] 1893.   [4] 1936.   [5] 1940.

3. Instinctive behaviour is set off by some specific external or internal factor.

The automatic character of instinctive action is not open to doubt because the disposition for such action is subject to variation; in other words there may be different degrees of preparedness to respond to the initiating factor; the level at which the stimulus makes its entry may vary. Like an organ, the instinct goes through an ontological development; in the young animal it is still undeveloped, or linked potentially with a certain condition, e.g. the maturity of the sex organs. This all tends to put it into the same category with the phenomena of physiological stimuli, already discussed. Lorenz (1937) underlined the automatic character of instinctive behaviour by comparing it to a machine running in neutral gear. The following is related to exemplify this:

It is related that a starling in a room empty of flies first went through the motions of looking for and catching flies, and then through those of swallowing them. Lorenz also gave an account of grey geese going through the motions of searching for and swallowing their food of aquatic plants in a pond empty of such plants, though their food was in fact in a bowl on the side. These are typical examples of "neutral gear" reactions. The way they run on to completion and all to no purpose is eloquent testimony to the automatic character of instinctive action. The action of female rats in bringing back to the nest young ones that have been removed from it is precisely similar. If one of the young rats is removed from the nest and laid down at some distance from it, the mother brings it back to the nest. If young rats, belonging to other mothers, are set beside the first baby rat when it is removed from the nest, the mother brings them all in. It is possible by this means to induce a mother rat to give hospitality in the nest to as many as thirty or forty young ones—a number of young she could never rear. It would appear from this that instinctive behaviour is a sort of vital automatism.

Animals do not learn to perform instinctive actions. They

know to begin with. When the mother of Fabre's[6] burrowing wasps carried out the instinctive actions of providing for her young, the young had not yet been formed; they were just eggs in her ovary. Lorenz (1937) pointed to the complicated and ingenious building of nests by birds; for the most part, this, too, is instinctive. Young birds building for the first time build as well as old birds. Carmichael (1926) kept the larvae of certain amphibians in a state of narcosis. This did not hinder their growth in any way. When they had reached an advanced stage of development he allowed them to emerge from their stupefied state. Their movements in swimming were just as finished and expert as those of their fellows of the same age, that had long been practising. Instincts then can be neither learnt nor altered. All modes of behaviour which can be learnt or modified are essentially distinct from instinct and I see no advantage here in using the term instinct for "plastic actions". Thus the concept instinct is clearly defined.

Now as to the relationship between instinct and reflex action, it is evident that the chief difference lies in the extremely complicated nature of instinctive behaviour. Ziegler (1920) was of the opinion that instinctive action is a chain reflex which one has to picture something like this: An organ of perception is stimulated by some external or some endogenous factor; it thereupon excites not one but many nerve paths which in their turn activate a correspondingly numerous set of action-organs. One must also assume the existence of a number of cross-linkages; the first action itself acts as a stimulating factor for another chain of stimulation resulting in action; this in its turn may set off another chain of reflexes. This makes instinctive behaviour into a complete mosaic of separate reflex actions, and thus reflex actions become the elements out of which this behaviour is constructed. Is the difference between instinct and reflex action merely qualitative then? A clear-cut decision meets with considerable difficulties which arise from the different methods of approach to the two

[6] 1879–1910.

sorts of phenomena. Reflex action depends upon morphological facts; organs of perception and response are linked by nerves. Our knowledge of instinct, on the other hand, is based on observation of animal behaviour. Physiological methods are here out of the question. Furthermore it is often difficult to decide whether certain phenomena are instinctive or reflex actions. Bethe (1931) studied the movement of crabs in walking and swimming. Such complicated reflex actions are here involved that, considering their behaviouristic effect, we should be inclined to regard such actions as instinctive. Aloys Kreidl (1904) proved, however, that the position of these crabs in relation to the earth is fixed by reflex actions and nothing else. In normal circumstances the underside of his crabs was turned towards the ground. This, he showed, was due entirely to the pressure of a statolith in an organ for maintaining equilibrium. He replaced the statolith by some iron filings and placed the crab in a magnetic field; the animal automatically turned its underside to the magnet. A simple stimulus produced a simple response. All the same there is no doubt that in the movement of these crabs a number of reflex actions were combined; the movements of the numerous legs must differ on each occasion —just as in the reflex action of the brainless frog's "wiping" movement. In both cases there are undoubtedly a number of correlated reflexes. It is a reasonable conclusion that there is a gradual transition from reflex action to instinct.

Nevertheless we must not allow a real distinction to escape our notice here. In the reflex, the course of the stimulus is straightforward; the excitation travels directly to the organ of response. The quality of the response corresponds to the quality of the stimulus. But the case becomes more complicated when a simple stimulus travels from the organ of perception to the central nervous system and is distributed along many nerve channels, so that numerous responsive actions occur. As behaviour, this will appear as follows: A single, simple stimulus such as a chemical irritant calls forth a reaction on the part of many organs. Have we here the beginnings of an instinct? It seems reasonable to suppose that we have.

Let us consider two quite concrete cases. The first is a typical reflex. A chemical stimulus results in the secretion of mucus by a gland. This stimulus is important biologically because the mucus counteracts the harmful effects of the chemical. The secretion of mucus does not occur unless the body is in some danger from the chemical. The response occurs, therefore, only when the harmful stimulus is present. Here again we see the biological co-ordination between stimulus and response—a chain of causation under the direction of living processes.

Let us look at the second case: A simple stimulus is carried along several channels to a number of organs of response, so that once more several results occur. For instance a chemical irritant causes not only the secretion of mucus from a gland but, simultaneously, a number of muscle contractions. As behaviour this will be seen as an escape reaction. We have here, as in the reflex, a co-ordination of stimulating cause and effect, but the effects, too, are co-ordinated. They work harmoniously together by simultaneously counteracting the harmful chemical and retreating from its neighbourhood. The flight reaction itself is a harmonious composition of many separate reactions. Moreover, in each particular instance the direction of flight will be determined by the way open and the position from which the stimulus comes. Yet flight will always take place in such a way as will best protect the organism. Thus a few free acid ions, acting as a stimulus, may bring about a very complicated operation. Each of the responses is co-ordinated with the stimulus; there are many reflexes but these too are co-ordinated, so that a new order of multiple reflexes is added to the order of the single reflex. We can add complication to complication by considering the behaviour of a tiny singing bird confronted by a bird of prey. We should call this typical instinctive behaviour.

Experiments have shown that the instinct of flight is aroused by the *shape* of the bird of prey. A bird is frightened without ever having seen its enemy before. The victim distinguishes between the peregrine falcon and the sparrowhawk and takes measures appropriate to avoid each bird. A large number of sight-cells in the retina receive a stimulus and the arrangement of the stimulated cells yields a form—that of the bird in flight. Any single part of it, i.e. any single stimulated sight-cell, or even detached features of the bird of prey, would be unable to produce the response to the stimulus. The instinctive flight reaction is aroused only by a quite specific arrangement of separate stimuli. It is to be noted that this panic fear is aroused by neither kestrel nor buzzard. A man, be it noted, would require a fair knowledge of field ornithology to distinguish at a glance between a peregrine falcon and a kestrel just appearing on the horizon. The singing bird never makes a mistake. This fact reveals how precise the connection is between the bird's instinctive behaviour and the peculiarities of its enemy. How does it come about that the response to this shape is so immediate, especially when no previous experience has taught the bird? The mechanism must be something like this: A series of sight cells, constantly changing, and varying in number from moment to moment with the flight of the two birds, join to form the image of the bird of prey. The single perceptions, combining together, form a shape like a mosaic. It is this shape that gives rise to the reaction. We can be sure of this because experimenters have replaced the birds of prey with paper kites resembling them. It is in the nature of instinct to be innate and characteristic for the species. For any particular image, therefore, a sort of specific potentiality must exist. The sensitivity to the image must be there, and must in a sense be awaiting its appearance. Once the shape appears upon the retina, the reaction follows—a reaction peculiar to the species and innate in it. This shape, previously delineated and awaited, has been called by Lorenz[7] the "innate schema". Thus, in the bird, there exists a shape-schema for falcons and one for sparrowhawks. These "schemata" arouse very different flight reactions in the various species of birds. The expert flyer hides when the falcon appears, and flies upwards on the approach of hawk or sparrowhawk. Observations reveal that all creatures gifted with instincts

[7] 1931, 1937a, b.

possess many such "schemata", so that it is possible to detect a good many of them representing enemies, friends, mate, prey, their young and, in social animals, fellow members of their species.

The distinctive marks are often simple colours; at other times they are complicated shapes like those of the enemies of the singing birds. The principle, however, is the same in every case.

It is clear that the "schema" corresponds to a quite definite behaviour pattern which, prior to all experience, is inborn. If we compare reflex with instinctive action, we can undoubtedly analyse the instinctive action into numerous reflexes. But are we justified in explaining instinctive action as a summation of reflexes? I must repeat once more what I said in regard to hormonal reactions: we dissociate, in order to analyse. The natural and orderly association of the reflexes in instinct is no less real than their separate existences. As we said before, synthesis must follow upon analysis, if science is not to fall into the error of generalizing from particular instances. Accordingly, the way in which reflexes are integrated in instinct reveals a purposive co-ordination, which the individual reflexes would never be able to create of themselves. Instinct arises, as it were, as a new and ordered compound, based on the co-existence and succession of a number of reflexes. The shaping of an instinct involves an order which is superimposed upon the order governing the single reflex. Single reflexes are co-ordinated and not only this, but the new combination is brought into relation with the environment of the creature.

It is true that instinctive action is purposive and directed to an end; yet it is not infallible, for its purpose is to react to the stimuli normal to the animal's environment. Every conceivable eventuality cannot be provided for. In instinct we see a fixed relationship between the animal and its environment. Instinct may be said to be purposive in the sense that it is directed to a particular end. Any analogy with consciously purposive human action would, of course, be out of place. Hormonal action, reflex action and instinctive action have **purposiveness** in common, though this does not imply any consciousness on the part of the animal engaging in purposive actions of these sorts. The care with which the wasp provides for her young, and the cunning with which the bird eludes its enemies, are not intellectual achievements; the animal does not possess the insight to see the purpose of what it does.

But can we be satisfied that instinct is no more than a harmonious integration of reflexes? In the instinctive actions of mating and caring for the young, we have to recognize that in addition to reflexes some hormonal reactions are involved. The mating-urge is related to the development and secretions of the sex glands. The character of the behaviour during the mating period is dependent upon the sex of the glands or the hormones they secrete. Hence it is clear that both hormonal and reflex actions play their part in instinct, which must be seen as the capacity to integrate into a higher order a number of reactions originating in two quite different ways.

5. ACTION BASED ON EXPERIENCE

Pavlov's[8] experiments in connection with conditioned reflexes in dogs laid the foundations of a widely-held theory. This theory is that all psychic activity is a result of a correlation of many separate reflexes. I reject this theory, as all I have written above will have made clear. The theory is based on an analysis followed by no synthesis, and a biological approach is incomplete without a synthesis.

I drew a sharp distinction between hormonal and reflex action because the processes were quite different. Instinctive action, too, differs from these—not because it consists of anything other than reflex and hormonal reactions, but because it stands on a higher level; it is a "compound" the components of which derive their character only from their relationship to the total instinctive action.

In the case of action based on experience, however, Pavlov was not only wrong in failing to synthesize the "compound".

[8] 1926, 1932 and see Andrep, 1927.

We are dealing here with something which is fundamentally different. Bierens de Haan (1940) spoke of a "plasticity of instincts", and Pavlov of a "plasticity of reflexes". My definition is at variance with both. Neither instincts nor reflex actions are plastic; at the most they may be counterfeited by others like themselves. "Plastic" implies the possibility of being changed; it assumes that a process can be modified—moulded or given a new stamp.

It seems perfectly clear that action resulting from various reflex actions is not plastic in the sense that an act which results from experience is, for we have to look elsewhere for the sphere within which plastic action can operate. Such expressions as "conditioned" reflexes or instincts might as well be eliminated from the start: they would have meaning only if there were such things as "unconditioned" reflexes and "unconditioned" instincts. Every reflex or instinct is set in motion by some factor or other: such a factor becomes the "condition" of the reflex or instinctive action. There is no such thing as a reaction without a cause. To speak of reflexes or instincts as conditioned is tautological.

Now this point is clear, we can consider what is meant by the plasticity of an action. In "plasticity" two factors are involved (a) the material awaiting an imprint or shape and (b) the thing that gives the form. We must remember, however, that we can never observe directly this process of plastic shaping or forming. All the biologist can see is concrete behaviour. He varies the relationship between the animal and its environment and endeavours to observe the co-ordination between the two. What he finds is that reflexes and instincts are rigidly and unchangingly linked with certain environmental factors. The link shows no sign of individuality. Above all, a reflex or instinct will manifest itself identical in action, every time the same individual is subjected to the same conditions. Even if a special feature should appear among the individuals of a species, this would not appear as something individually acquired, but would correspond rather to those individual peculiarities which distinguish to some extent every individual.

14

Thus both instinct and reflex are like a bodily organ which develops and grows, though present from birth.

Experiment, however, has taught us that under identical conditions the same individual may react differently on successive occasions. If we can be sure that the different reaction is not due to some alteration in the animal's physiology, such as fatigue or sexual maturity, we must look elsewhere for its cause. We find, in fact, that certain behaviour results from earlier experience. The action is not automatic, for the animal's behaviour is here motivated by its remembered experience. The most striking example is provided by the training of animals. When these are trained by punishment, they behave in such a way as to avoid punishment. When rewarded for certain actions, they remember this and act in such a way as to obtain pleasure. O. Koehler[9] managed by means of a rattle apparatus to train his pigeons never to peck up more than a fixed number of grains of corn. Von Frisch (1915) and Hertz[10] managed to induce their bees to show an interest in chessboards with varying numbers of squares, or in a square of a definite colour. Before their training, the bees were quite indifferent to these things. We can call actions of this sort "plastic", for a mode of acting which was not inborn is imprinted upon individuals.

How are we to look upon this natural phenomenon? What causes this individual formation, and what is the plastic material which is here moulded? It is clear that experience can be remembered. When Koehler's (1949) pigeon had eaten three grains of corn and was about to take a fourth, the ground beneath its feet shook. The desire for corn is an inborn one. When the pigeon was hungry it showed a tendency to eat anything looking like a grain of corn. But the rising of the floor set off a fear reaction. It is clear from Koehler's film that after some time the pigeon wants to pick up a fourth grain but does not dare to. The pigeon can not only count, but can memorize the unpleasant experience of the rising floor, and the fact that

[9] 1932, 1933, 1949.　　　　　　[10] 1929a, b; 1936, 1937.

when no more than three grains are eaten nothing unpleasant happens. Von Frisch's (1915) bees always found syrup in a blue or yellow chess-board square, so they made for the squares of these colours, even when there was no syrup there. The fact that these bees were found to treat red, green and light-grey squares identically shows that the bees are not only colour blind in respect to these colours but also that the act of obtaining food is connected by them with the blue or yellow squares.

Thus for the individual an order or relationship is established; it exists for him alone if he alone has had the experience. Things have been associated on several occasions. The association eventually becomes permanent. What animals experience, what they remember, we can judge only to the extent that we can recognize changes in their behaviour which are consequent upon experience. It is important to distinguish between this behaviour and instinctive behaviour. In instinct, the initial organization, peculiar to the species, determines the whole course of the action. In action based on experience behaviour takes account of a situation not yet actual. For example, Koehler's pigeons refused the fourth grain of corn before the floor beneath their feet started to quake. Experience alone, then, can originate actions of this sort.

How can something, felt previously, influence behaviour? The picture in the memory undoubtedly emits impulses which affect the animal's means of perception in much the same way as the real stimuli. For weeks on end I rode a horse along a certain road until one day a circus with a lion arrived at its junction with another road. From that day onwards the horse showed fear at that point. The place at which the horse once met the lion produced the same fear reaction ever afterwards, even though the lion was absent. The memory of the lion had the same effect as the real lion. The single occurrence must have persisted as an image of some sort. Thus the memory-image must be accepted as an objective fact. There is no question here of subjective experience.

The ability to act upon experience is based on the ability to retain experience and to make use of impulses deriving from these retained experiences. As regards experiences which do not reveal themselves in any specific action, we can express conclusions only in so far as they are our own personal experiences. We can know nothing of what goes on in animals. All we can do is to watch their behaviour; comparison and analogy are the sole sources of our knowledge. Konrad Lorenz[11] did much research which enabled him to draw a clear distinction between instinctive action and action based on experiences. It is due to his information that we may object to such ideas as "plastic instincts" and "plastic reflexes". While it is true that instincts and reflexes, like bodily organs, are subject to regulation, they are peculiar to each species and cannot be altered. Lorenz also showed that the same action can be instinctive in one case (and, in consequence, unalterable) and in another "plastic", and therefore capable of being influenced by experience. Lorenz showed, too, that an action may be partly instinctive and partly plastic. The reactions of the higher animals are largely of this sort. Opposed to this view is the idea that a certain behaviour is indeed instinctive and innate, but can later be modified by experience, and thus assimilated to action based on experience. Pavlov (1926) held this of the reflex and Bierens de Haan (1940) of instinct. This view, however, was entirely refuted by the discoveries of Lorenz (1937a). According to him instinctive actions occur with no dependence upon experience whatsoever; where, however, a plastic imprint is possible, no instinctive norm is at work. If in one species a mode of behaviour is instinctive, and in another dependent on experience, this is due entirely to specific difference. In the same species, experience can be acquired only in that sphere where instinct is absent. The ability to gather experiences is as it were a gap or hole waiting to be filled by experience. A little while ago we spoke of a "schema" as that faculty for initiating instinctive action and bringing sense-impressions into a single whole. This schema can be shaped in advance, like the schema of the bird of prey in the singing

[11] 1931, 1935, 1937a, b; 1941, 1943.

bird. But it is also possible that such a "schema" is created as a result of experience. Lorenz caused eggs of the Turkish duck to be hatched by grey geese. The young ducks exhibited a social instinct in regard to other members of their own species. But when they grew to sexual maturity they did not seek their partners among their fellows, but among the grey geese. This implies that the social "schema" was inborn, while the sex-partner "schema" was imprinted by experience. That which decided the duck's sex-partner "schema" was its familiarity with the grey geese when it was young. In natural circumstances it would have spent its youth among members of its own species. In the case of birds which are strictly monogamous, the sex-partner schema is imprinted by the sight of one particular individual in a very special period of its life. In the case of some animals reared by human hands, the human nurse has been looked upon as the sex-partner, even when members of the same species have been available. These examples show that action based on experience must be quite radically different from instinctive action. Our question as to the material which experience moulds is to some extent answered. The capacity to acquire experience, in respect of certain definite matters, is inborn; it takes the form of a substratum which awaits its moulding at the hands of experience.

If with this in mind we consider Pavlov's[12] experiments, we shall find that he was dealing with a complex of heteronomous components. Pavlov studied the reflex action of saliva secretion in dogs, and established that a number of quite distinct factors are concerned with this secretion which is undoubtedly a reflex action. It is usually the smell of food which stimulates the secretion of saliva. Pavlov caused the giving of food to be preceded by all sorts of stimuli quite unconnected with food or eating. Among these were the ringing of bells or even feelings of pain. He found that these preliminaries were capable of stimulating the secretion of saliva. Accordingly, Pavlov and his followers called saliva secretion a "conditioned

[12] 1926, 1932.

reflex" since it can be associated with definite external influences. Arguing from this fact, the followers of Pavlov maintained that the whole psychic life of an animal can be broken up into chains of conditioned reflexes. I have already shown how inappropriate the description "conditioned" is; there cannot be an unconditioned reflex; the only difference between reflexes is that some are conditioned exogenously, others endogenously. In these observations of Pavlov we are clearly dealing with a combination of two heteronomous phenomena. The reflex action of secreting saliva was linked with a condition which preceded it, one which had to be experienced. Training, as in the case of these dogs, was only possible when experience could be gained. Pavlov's dogs were trained to react to thrice-repeated clangs and to a definite pitch of sound. Saliva secretion ensued even when no food was given. What Pavlov called "conditioned" we, to be consistent, must describe as the result of training, for it depends upon a capacity for being taught. Hence the reflex of saliva secretion was set off by a "schema" imprinted by experience.

But Pavlov was able to bring about the same effect, i.e. saliva secretion, by inducing an "unconditioned" (!) reflex. For saliva secretion occurred automatically as soon as food was placed in the dog's mouth, even when the motor part of the brain had been removed. In this case the secretion was conditioned by a reflex, which in its turn was conditioned by the stimulation of the taste buds. This is apparently the reason why so many text-books describe this reaction as an "unconditioned" reflex.

It is unnecessary to labour the point that this reflex, occurring after the removal of the motor part of the brain, is a reflex in the sense defined above. There was a simple reflex arc proceeding from the organ of perception to the organ of response.

Thus there are here two reflex systems at work, that of the simple reflex arc and that based on a "schema" developed as a result of experience. The two tend to be confused because the result is the same.

Rohracher (1947) drew our attention to another very instructive example. When a man comes out of the darkness into the light, his pupils contract. This—quite automatic—action is the pupil reflex. Furthermore, he closes his eyelids: this is doubtless an action controlled by several reflex systems. A man can close his eyes voluntarily—with and without good reason, even in this case. On the other hand, if the stimulation is strong enough, he will be forced to close his eyes quite automatically. In addition, he can cover his eyes with his hand. The way in which he does this—with left hand or right, with flat hand or crooked, or with a book held in the hand—is entirely under his control, just as the action itself is. The hands need not be raised at all. The eyelids, however, provide an example of how the same mechanism of response can be excited by different reaction systems and yet perform the same action. One system can replace another, and either is capable of modifying the response.

The reaction that takes place on the basis of experience is thus linked up with both reflexes and instincts. An experience can introduce either a reflex or an instinct; it can be inserted between two reflex actions or two instinctive actions and it can play its part in the final action. In one species the whole reaction series can be instinctive, and is therefore inborn and rigid. In another species, a small part of the reaction can be decided on the basis of experience. Finally, experience can play the major part in the reactions as a whole. In this case we see an instinctive action resulting from causes in which reflexes and instincts play a very minor part. Lorenz called this nexus of causes "interlocking". Experience, of course, results in habit formation so that action finally becomes purely automatic. In action based on experience "practice makes perfect"; in instinctive action perfection is a free gift from heaven above.

6. INTELLIGENT ACTION

In human behaviour we find all the three types of reaction we have considered at work: hormonal, reflex and instinctive.

Are all types of human behaviour covered under these three headings?

Let us consider a baby who has a completely new experience. He discovers for example a new object. We find that he investigates the unknown object and plays with it until he has discovered a use for it. At first sight, there appears to be nothing particularly human about this. W. Köhler's (1921) anthropoid apes tried out boxes placed one on top of the other or sticks until they reached the bananas they wanted. We cannot limit this sort of behaviour to anthropoid apes and human beings. Nor can we say that anthropoid apes resemble men, not only morphologically, but also as regards behaviour. Even birds will be found to try out unfamiliar objects until they have discovered a use for them. Such behaviour is by no means uncommon. It has an element of instinct in it. This "appetence behaviour", as some biologists have called it, has been observed even among the invertebrates. It consists in a groping, blind sort of testing, often set in motion by a physiological condition, which persists until the object being investigated either sets off an instinctive "schema" or gives the animal a pleasant or unpleasant experience and so imprints a new "schema". There is no doubt that such "appetence behaviour" plays an important part even in human beings. But this does not justify us in thinking that human behaviour is nothing more than a complex of appetent tendencies developed to a tremendous degree. In animals the result is either the excitation of an instinct or an experience; it is always a situation which as such is laid down in advance.

A human infant makes use of things, alters them and fits them to his purposes in a way quite unconnected with instinct or experience. He does not only seek and find a situation; he invents it. In this respect human behaviour is quite unlike animal behaviour, for, as he grows older, the child in his play imagines things that have never happened, and looks for objects which will help him, when worked upon, to realize the picture or form that he has thought out. He does, in other words, what artists and inventors do professionally. W. Köhler's

(1921) ape tests something, and discovers something; the human being thinks of something and invents something. Looking at things from a purely zoological viewpoint, A. Portmann[13] recognized the unique position of man in respect of behaviour, and has expressed himself in regard to this far better than any non-scientist has done for a long time.

If one accepts the thesis that biology is incapable of describing the human being because it can see only the animal in man, one does so without good reason. This thesis is based on mere prejudice. If one accepts this, one has to accept a number of similar conclusions, for instance, that because the Arts start with man they must inevitably see human affairs everywhere; because physics sets out from things physical it can see things only in terms of physics. My object in this book has been to build upon the most general truths and, with these as a firm foundation, to reveal the plurality of the law systems at work in the sphere of life. I began with molecules but endeavoured to show the special case of living matter. Now I feel justified in making the behaviour of plants and animals the starting point for my consideration of human behaviour. In my effort to establish an immaterial principle of life, I am not content to assume that we are doomed to perpetual ignorance. Similarly I fail to see any logical limitations arising from the mere fact that human beings are superior to animals. It is true that the biological aspect of human nature is but one of the aspects open to investigation. Yet it is this biological aspect which, provided we avoid generalizations and dogmatism, reveals most clearly man's status as a living being, and which shows up his special position and the special standards applicable to his relations with his environment.

Otto Storch (1948) has recently proved man's unique biological position from a new standpoint: An animal is born into and confined in a circle which is prescribed for it by its organs of perception; it lives in its environment in accordance with a standard fixed by its genom. Storch called this circle the

[13] 1944, 1946.

"function-circle". Man, too, is born into such a function-circle, but is not confined to it. He has burst its bonds. Man is not so much born into an environment; he has, as it were, built his own.

Man disposes of an armoury of reflexes and instincts, and possesses in an extraordinarily high degree the capacity to collect experiences. If the human being were just another animal, his mode of behaving would be determined in just one way. But these factors, fixed or plastic, do not determine man's behaviour in any particular way. Man's relationship with his biotope is not prescribed by instinct or experience; it is fixed by man himself. Unlike animals, man is capable of living in all possible and by no means predictable relationships with his environment.

We must consider here the simple way in which an animal lives in relation to its fellows—either as a gregarious or a solitary being, either monogamously or polygamously, according to species. But in man there is the widest possible divergence among all nations and among the individuals of any one nation. This cannot be explained in terms of either instinct or experience. The part which the individual plays in his environment is not imposed by nature, but is chosen by himself. So far as instinct and experience go, man forms a part of the same world as animals, but instinct and experience do not exercise compulsion upon him; they act merely as directives. Hence the rôle played by a man in life, compared with that of an animal, can be quite purposeless and deplorable. The human being can act the fool. The utmost an animal can do is to act, by chance, inappropriately.

Man has in addition the ability to perform "plastic" actions, which are somewhat more than actions based on experience. Some material capable of being moulded is present which was not inborn. Since the shaper of this material is not simply experience it must be something else. As in the case of action based on experience, connections between things are established, and these are provided by experience, because the things have once been related in the memory. Such connections exist already in the form of reflexes and instincts. The connections which the human being establishes between himself and his environment, however, were never before experienced; hence he is not in a position to copy them; we should be inclined to say that he invented them. It is obvious, however, that these connections are possible ones, even if they are not already pre-formed. These possibilities, real or potential, must be recognizable in advance, as recognizable as events really experienced. An illustration will make this clear.

By his "appetent" behaviour, as in play, an ape can acquire some experience with a stick. Everything that happens when he is using the stick builds up for him a mass of experience, and he is able to repeat actions with the stick which he has previously performed. Nothing, however, which does not look like a stick can be employed in a similar manner, because it has no conceivable connection with a stick. Nothing can be done with the stick deliberately either, unless it has already happened. These were the facts W. Köhler (1921) discovered about his apes. Sticks joined together produce a long stick. Anything which was not reached with a short stick had been reached with a long stick; hence in the future it will be reached with a long stick.

That which is already there is, therefore, the memory image of the stick and the experience obtained with it. But one can make sticks from a tree or from a floor of laths, only if one sees that sticks can be made from the boughs of trees or from the loosened laths of a floor. Furthermore a stick can be used for purposes other than those already discovered, purposes which bring it into relation with other things. Its weight, for example, may make it appear appropriate as a counterpoise.

Human actions are often of the nature of the above. This is what may be called intelligent action. The actuality is recognized from potentialities which have never previously been actualized; the actuality has never been the object of perception; it cannot possibly be found in the memory. It has to be invented. If one is to recognize what is not known, one must have knowledge of everything that could be done with the given object; one must know of the potentiality awaiting realization. There must be some insight into the real nature of the thing. We call this faculty of recognizing the essential characteristics of something "intelligence". Of course, experience is necessary before intelligence can come to exist. Experience leads to two different things: first to the reproduction of chains of experience; secondly to that insight which perceives the essential characteristics of things, and which recognizes these characteristics once more, when they appear in quite different objects. Intelligence is based on abstraction, as does all perception of a thing's essential nature. It is intelligence, insight, which teaches us that A and B produce C. It is thus possible to anticipate C from A and B. Intelligence makes it possible to see that A and B contain within themselves the possibility of C—even when C has never been an object of experience.

What here takes the place of experience, and shapes the action that follows, is insight into a logical connection—for we can now go so far as to say this. For the moment this is enough to establish action based on insight as one of the norms or types of reaction. Intelligent action depends first upon insight into the real nature of things; secondly, it is concerned with conceptual and abstract thought (e.g. both a stone and a piece of metal are heavy and can both act as paperweights); thirdly, it involves the ability to imagine things—things never yet experienced and yet possible of realization. Thus intelligence gives a freedom of existence: things purely imaginary can be called into objective existence.

VIII

LIFE'S ORDERED RELATIONSHIP

1. LIFE'S ORDERED RELATIONSHIP

WE have up to now tried to mark the single types of reaction sharply off from one another and to demonstrate their plurality. We want now to find out what it is they all have in common.

In popular language we say that spring flowers push their heads "inquisitively" out of the soil, or that plants turn their leaves "longingly" towards the light. The snail is "frightened" when he draws in his horns; the "pitiless" hawk slaughters the partridge; the "cunning" fox "takes care" not to be caught in the trap. There is a naïvety in these expressions. It consists in failing to recognize the different laws which govern the reactions seen, and in ascribing human feeling and intelligence to creatures that do not possess them. All these actions are directed towards a goal—a goal which is quite obvious to the human observer. But the various modes of behaviour, as we have seen, are based on widely differing physico-chemical principles.

The most widely different kinds of plants and animals are sensitive to light either positively or negatively. Yet there are other animals and plants which are quite indifferent to light. Moreover light is absorbed in very different ways—by means of carotin, spots of pigment, epithelial cells sensitive to light, or eyes. The means by which the light is transmitted varies greatly. The resultant action may be muscular action, movements of flagella or growth. Amid all this variety the one thing that is common is that light is in each case aiding or endangering life. In the case of creatures which are indifferent to it, light exerts no influence upon them.

The organs of perception place the living organism in a

definite relationship with the factors of the environment which thus become for it stimuli. Response to these stimuli brings the organism into the most favourable situation for maintaining life and enables it to keep out of danger. The goal of all the creature's actions is to secure the optimum conditions for maintaining its life. There are obvious exceptions to this: the flying of insects into the flame of a lamp, or the opening of buds on a fine winter's day. But this does not prove that these reactions have no proper purpose. These exceptions are interesting in that they prove that the living creature is not able to tackle all possible situations: it is fitted only to deal with those normal to its environment or with those most likely to occur. The advantages insects gain by living together, dogs from hunting in packs, or most creatures have from defending their young are obvious. It is no less obvious that life in a confined space would be injurious to other creatures whose food is widely scattered. If the sparrow took flight at the sight of every larger bird, it would never be doing anything else. If a bird waited to be convinced of the dangerous nature of the hawk by actual experience, it would never have a chance to make use of that experience.

However we look at the matter, we cannot overlook the fact, for the sake of the materialistic dogma of chance, that each single reaction is determined by a principle of order, which implies an ordered relationship between living organisms and their environments, between the environmental stimuli and the behaviour of the living creatures. All types of reaction, then, have one thing in common—purposiveness, operation according to a plan.

The fact that all types of reaction are directed to the same end must not obscure the other fact—that they are heteronomous in relation one to the other. The form or "morphe", too, as appropriate to a particular way of life, serves to achieve the same end as behaviour. It is not explicable except in terms of its purpose. Its parts are so related that the result is a harmonious functioning of the organism as a whole. We have noticed the same thing in the reactivity of cells and of the organs built up from them. The various parts of the morphe react with one another; they influence one another. This leads to what Hesse[1] called "ent-harmony". The environment is, in very different ways, included in this harmonious working or excluded from it, and this, too, happens in accordance with an orderly plan. By this means the "eph-harmony" is brought into existence. It is clear that "ent-" and "eph-harmony" are but different aspects of the same harmony, which is served by all the very various modes and systems of reaction.

We have thus established that every reaction of an animate thing is itself a co-ordination of many tiny physico-chemical processes. We have demonstrated, furthermore, that all sorts of reactions taken together form a completely orderly whole within the organism's capacity for reaction.

The ordered relationship of the separate physico-chemical processes and the ordered relationship of the separate reaction chains is reminiscent of the conclusions we reached in defining the chemo-dynamic wholeness-factor and the living form. We saw then how molecules, cells and, finally, multicellular organisms were built up one by one in an orderly manner, so that a progressively higher order was constituted. We have now seen how principles of order are at work in the living system itself. *But the principles of adaptation and reaction operate far beyond the confines of the organism. There is a co-ordination with the environment as well. The purposiveness we see extends not only to the relation of the parts to the whole, but also to the integration of the whole with external nature.*

2. THE UNITY IN LIVING PROCESSES

All the foregoing considerations have led to the conclusion that the phenomena of life are unique. The laws governing animate processes are not just special instances of the laws that govern inanimate nature. We have regarded as conclusive only those arguments which are applicable equally to inanimate processes.

[1] 1935, 1943.

Our method was to examine and test the laws we found operating in the living organism. In natural science the laws which govern the existence of something are the criterion of its nature. It was our aim to show that the laws governing animate things are different from those governing inanimate matter. The following conclusion is therefore permissible:

The laws governing life differ from those governing inanimate matter. The difference implies a difference of nature. Life stands upon a level of being higher than the phenomena of inanimate matter. Hence animate matter is radically different from inanimate matter.

We took our proofs from four groups of phenomena; hence we have four proofs of the uniqueness of life, not one.

We first examined the chemical processes at work in the organism. We saw there the biodynamic factor of wholeness, associated with the tendency to instability in the chemical phenomena—a tendency unknown in inanimate matter. By means of this instability the individual processes were brought under a central control so that a unity was created.

We next went on to show that the "morphe" was a pre-stabilized space and time form which becomes objective in influencing the material particles. On the other hand the morphe shows an ability to adapt itself to its surroundings, or rather, it reveals that it fits its surroundings. By this means the ecological law of place-relationship was established. We were finally able to show that the ability of the organism to react constituted a further ordered relationship with the changes in its environment. In developing each of these four proofs we set out from a different point. In one case, we began with atomic and molecular structure, and by way of micells, arrived at the dynamic structure of the living organism. In the second instance, we considered the shape form, the appearance of the organism, as our fundamental phenomenon, and lighted upon the laws which govern the "morphe". We then looked for a beetle under a stone and confirmed that both had an origin, but only the beetle had a purpose. Finally, in the capacity to react, we again considered changes in the organism. All four ways have yielded results, but can we say that all four led to the same goal? Are the four results in fact one result? We might say that life obeys laws not found in inanimate matter and yet maintain that there is a multiplicity of such "law-abiding" systems. In linking adaptability and irritability together under the same heading, we tried to show that these two express the same purposive relationship. It is possible, however, that all the other phenomena of life converge upon one another. Each one of them serves to explain all the others.

We can, for instance, see everything as a chemical process. The development of the morphe is undoubtedly the result of metabolic processes. The life of the cell, the relation of cytoplasm to nucleus, the power of regeneration, cell division, the co-ordination of cells in the metabiont—all these result, to a large extent, from interacting chemical influences, which have metabolism as their sole basis. Similarly every adaptation to environment is an expression of some chemical situation. Life could quite reasonably be described as a wonderful co-ordination of chemical reactions.

But no chemical reaction could be dominated from a living centre unless that "initial organization" existed of which Moyse spoke. It is the "morphe", the ordered relationship of the materials in space, which conditions the way the materials react. If molecules are to play their appointed rôles in the organism, they must first exist as "tools" of the organism.

The organic molecules in the organism are also components of the morphe. It is only in the morphe that they can arise or continue to exist. The morphe produces the "inorganic situation" (replaced in the chemical laboratory by complicated apparatus) which synthesizes them.

The fundamental or general adaptation to environment is simply the adaptation of the morphe to its environment: it is simply that aspect of the morphe which is related to the surroundings.

With regard to the ability to react we were able to show

15

that it is, potentially, already stabilized: a reflex, for example, runs an appointed course, one prescribed by the morphe.

Instinct grows and ripens like an organ of the body. It is a complex of reflexes and hormonal reactions under the dominion of the morphe.

Experience and intelligent action have the power to intervene in what experiments show to be a gap between reactions. This, too, must be provided for in the morphe.

The harmonious collaboration of the parts of the organism implies that the parts fit together or are fundamentally adapted one to the other. We saw too that the parts are made to fit their environment. Ent-harmony and eph-harmony dominate all living activity. It is even possible to affirm that the catalyst is adapted to the molecule upon which it works. Thus there is nothing outside the scope of such planned adaptation.

The evolution theory teaches us that this fundamental adaptation, of the parts one to another and of the whole to the world outside, is the product of phylogenetic development. Hence we can describe this development too as a general expression of the capacity for reaction. In morphogenesis the cells exert influence one upon another; they in their turn are guided by the body's entelechy. The parts of the cell, organelles or molecules, are directed to a particular type of reaction by the order governing the cell. Thus action and reaction are characteristic of life in all its aspects. The term reaction is used in chemistry as well as in the physiology of stimuli. We made it plain, of course, that the molecules in the organism "react" in the vital sense, and so reaction, the ability to react, extends right into the microscopic sphere of life. Everything that occurs results from this "reactability" and everything is an expression of the causal influence of one constituent upon another.

Thus the four points of view from which we studied life are in fact four aspects of a single system of laws. Hence in speaking of the uniqueness of life we had in mind its uniform character. This uniformity is that which marks it off from inanimate matter.

3. IMMANENCE AND TRANSCENDENCE

Rickert, in *Die Grenzen der naturwissenschaftlichen Begriffs-bildung* (1921) wrote as follows:

The moment one thinks of an organism as a chemical or physical process, or even as a purely mechanical complex of atoms, one leaves the sphere of biology; one has ceased to look at organisms as organisms. One does this sort of thing when one regards the chemical elements, or heat and light, merely as atoms in motion; for in this case, too, the elements cease to be elements in the more restricted sense, and nothing remains of heat and light, that warms and illuminates. The thermal and optical aspects are overlooked. Contradictions appear only when the biologist, *qua* biologist, seeks to regard organisms purely mechanistically, for he then overlooks the very qualities in the object which made it the subject of a special science—biology.

We have thought of the organism as a chemical or physical process, and have endeavoured to define it as a purely mechanical complex of atoms. According to Rickert we have not only left the sphere of biology; we have not even entered it. Nevertheless we have discovered that life is "a law unto itself". It seems reasonable to point out, therefore, that vitalism and mechanism are not merely matters of one's point of view, that the result one obtains is not determined by the position from which one sets out. On the contrary, it was my express aim in the first part of this book to bring forward with all their weight the arguments which favour mechanism. Anybody who read just the first few pages of my book might easily come to the conclusion that I was a mechanist. On the contrary, by pursuing the mechanistic arguments and the evidence supporting them, we actually reached the vitalist position. We allowed atoms to be atoms and molecules, molecules. We started from them, and reached vitalism. It was clearly no subjective standpoint that determined the course of our proofs. Our questions were: 1. What course do the chemical processes take? 2. How does the form arise? 3. At what point does the organism appear and what does it look like? 4. What does it do? All our arguments were concerned with the discussion of these points.

We endeavoured to exclude subjective judgments and anthropomorphism. We used terms like realization and potentiality, immanence and transcendence, purposiveness and wholeness as concepts proper to natural science. Some people regard the use of such terms in science as questionable. But must we really avoid using a word like "purposiveness" simply because it originally meant striving to reach a goal upon which one had set one's eye? I would rather be blamed for a touch of psychism than for obscurity. We are bound to use the terms we know in describing what comes our way. It is impossible for us to measure nature with "inhuman" ideas; we have to make use of human measurements. What we express in this way are relationships, but they can be no more than analogies.

"Immanent" describes in the first place all that is within me, all that proceeds from me, all that is inherent in any way within me. All that is outside me, apart from me, or independent of me, is "transcendent". Thus, in saying that some physical process is immanent in matter, I mean that everything is potentially present in it, which will be realized by the chemical reactions which ensue. That is all. If on the other hand, I say that life is transcendent in regard to matter, I mean no more than that life does not inhere in matter, just as something which is independent of me is not in me. Life is not immanent in matter but it is immanent in the cell. Although one is forced to use such expressions, it does not follow that they carry all the meaning with which they have become associated in the course of history. "Transcendent" means no more than "outside me", but it does not imply the existence of something independent and self-sufficient. Thus the cell's life is not immanent in its matter; it is immanent in the cell. It cannot be found elsewhere. Again the life of the total organism is not immanent in the cells; it transcends them. We can, therefore, conclude that "development" always presupposes the immanence of many potentialities of development. If development proceeds along lines independent of immanent potentialities, we cannot believe that such are responsible for it. We are thus forced to accept the existence of transcendent as well as immanent potentialities. Similarly and for the same reasons it is impossible to regard the substantial form as a kind of species *logos*, as an entity outside or above the species' individual members. Thus I find it impossible to believe that the entelechy is an entity transcendent in relation to the organism. I am therefore led to the conclusion that the entelechy is an individual principle of order which does not presuppose an anterior existence as substantial form.

I have described animate matter as differing radically from inanimate matter, and as occupying a different level of being. If we ascribe exclusive validity to either animate or inanimate matter we are acting subjectively. We overlook the uniqueness of that which we are trying to explain. This is well illustrated by two theorists. One, A. March (1948), makes biology into a branch of physics, and the other, Meyer-Abich (1948), makes physics a branch of biology. The one makes life a derivation of inanimate matter; the other makes inanimate matter a derivative of life.

4. WHOLENESS

Though we did not begin our study with the idea of examining the wholeness principle we finished by establishing that a wholeness does exist. Nowadays the question of wholeness is one of the most live issues in intellectual discussion. It is discussed in the spheres of political economy, sociology and even cosmology. In each case the discussion turns upon a word which can be used more or less arbitrarily. In consequence, we must be clear as to what we mean by "wholeness".

During our enquiry we encountered two sorts of wholeness, each quite different from the other. One was the merogenously constituted wholeness of inanimate things. Here there was a merogenous multiplicity, a merogenous principle; the correlation of the forces immanent in the parts created the whole. Opposed to this is the living whole which is constituted by a hologenous principle, the entelechial factor of wholeness. It is this factor which binds parts together which would never be fashioned into a whole by the forces immanent in them. This factor of wholeness is transcendent in relation to the separate material components. Let us recall that the entelechy is not itself a wholeness mingling with matter and inducing it to participate in the wholeness. Rather, it is the *forma corporis* which with the material parts forms a whole. The parts are governed by the laws operating in the whole. All the laws governing the parts are subordinated to the whole. The parts by themselves are incapable of forming a whole.

Driesch (1928) considered that it is impossible to define wholeness. It is, he thought, indefinable because it is a fundamental, an ultimate concept. Driesch held that one can see from the beginning that the parts belong to a whole. Consequently relationship to a whole is one of their qualities. In fact relationship to a whole is the quality which for Driesch distinguished all the parts of the whole. He said that a composite object may be called a whole if, as soon as something is taken from it, it loses its essential character. It would appear that for Driesch being composite is essential for wholeness. This seems to hold in the sphere of inanimate things. If one H atom is detached from a water molecule, the water molecule loses its essential nature. It is now governed by the quite different laws of the hydroxyl group, OH.

If we regard wholeness as a purely logical concept, it expresses the relationship of the concept to its distinguishing marks, which are one and the same thing as the concept. Burkamp's (1929) definition of wholeness corresponds with this: the whole is not compounded from parts, but parts of it can be distinguished. Burkamp went on to describe wholeness as conditioned by its meaning and to define it as structure cut off from what is around it. He linked this quality of being bounded and separate with the idea of wholeness. In other words wholeness implies a certain isolation, a certain independence. Driesch referred repeatedly to Kant's definition of wholeness but thought that Kant never really determined what wholeness is. He thought that Kant was familiar with the idea of wholeness, in fact that it dominated all his teaching, but that he never defined it nor realized that it was indefinable. These are Kant's words:

> By system I mean the subsuming under one idea of numerous elements of perception. This is the rational concept of the form of a whole: both the extent of the manifold elements and the position of the parts are determined *a priori*. Included in the scientific and rational concept are the purpose and form of the corresponding whole. The unity of purpose which unites all the parts in the idea of the whole is such that no element in the knowledge of the rest can be dispensed with, nor can these be any chance addition or any unlimited growth; everything has its limits determined *a priori*. The whole is therefore articulated (*articulatio*) and not just heaped up (*coacervatio*).[2]

I can now see what made Driesch so sensible of the difficulty of using this definition. Driesch was very careful to avoid anything that savoured of psychism. In the last chapter I said that analogies with psychic experiences could legitimately be drawn, provided we were certain that we could find a real relationship, and were aware that we were assessing the facts in human terms. Surely we can apply this principle when thinking of wholeness. I have, I think, pointed out quite analogous circumstances in the objective sphere, in so far as the subject matter of logic can ever be compared with purely objective facts.

Driesch was thinking of something composite, of the abstraction "compositeness", while the logical definitions are concerned with the unity of which the part is merely an aspect. It almost appears as though Driesch with his definition of wholeness, came near to my merogenously-constituted "wholeness": that is, indeed, in principle and essence, something composite.

In a whole which is merogenously constituted, those particles of matter which form a whole through the forces immanent in them become something different the moment they show themselves as governed by other laws. Oxygen, once in the water molecule, does not show itself conformable to the same laws as it does in the elementary state. It has become something

[2] *Critique of Pure Reason.*

different. If one can call an atom a whole in my sense of the term, it has now become something else according to Driesch's definition of wholeness, because "we call a composite object a whole if it loses its essential character when something is taken from it."[3] Driesch, it is true, was thinking in terms of logic. An analogy may help here: an electron is taken from sodium and one is added to fluorine if they join to produce sodium fluoride. Hence, in this sense, sodium and fluorine are not the same as in their elementary state. The appositeness of Aloys Wenzl's (1938) definition is now apparent. He would in this case speak of wholes but he would call them wholes due to arrangement. The arrangement is altered and so the "whole thing", the atom, is altered, since it is arrangement that constitutes the whole. But are we here concerned with a fundamental "otherness"? Obviously not, because it is in each case the same material particle which is undergoing change. In the passage from one state to another a new principle of order comes to hold sway. It abolishes the previous one, but it is merely a principle of arrangement. The atom, therefore, has not changed radically; it has simply re-arranged its parts. This would be the "whole due to arrangement" of Aloys Wenzl (1938) which corresponds to my "merogenously constituted whole". Let us now consider the gene in that living whole, the cell. For this purpose we may say that the gene is a particle of matter forming part of a nucleoprotein molecule. But because the gene has become incorporated in the nucleoprotein it does not imply that it has become radically different. But its relation to other matter *has* become radically different. The part played by the gene is one of order and relationship. It can really only be isolated from the order governing the whole it inhabits by a process of abstraction. Thus the total order, the whole, is not, as Driesch suggested, something composite, a whole based solely on the relationship of the parts; the principle governing it is itself a whole. The separate members of the "whole due to arrangement" which manifest themselves

---

[3] *Philosophie des Organischen*, 1938, Leipzig.

in the movements and in the behaviour of the material parts, must be described in the Kantian sense as "articulated". We speak here only of analogy; all the same, we can clearly discern that, in life, the relationship of the members to the whole is exactly similar to that of the characteristics or "accidents" to the concept, in logic.

If the matter in the living organism is taken over functionally into a radically different sphere of being, this does not mean that it loses any of its special character as matter. It means that something is superimposed upon it. The entelechial life-principle seizes upon matter, takes possession of it and determines it in a special way. Thus in the metabiont we came upon a form of being in which an entelechial order of wholeness lays hold on, not atoms and molecules, but cells which are themselves already governed on entelechial principles, and are already living individuals. We recognized the principle of order as a dynamic ordering of the individual to the whole.

We saw, too, that the part was explicable only in terms of the whole and that this principle has a far wider bearing when ecology is considered. The fish fits into water as its environment. It is explicable only in such terms as "breathing in the water", or "swimming in the water". The insect is adapted to the flower in a similar way. The relationship is brought about, as we know, by adaptation and a system of reactions. The living creature can be neither understood nor explained in isolation from its environment. Would it not be possible to regard an ecological unit, a living community, as a whole of superior rank? But if we do this we shall have to include in this new whole the inanimate elements in the environment as well. We should find ourselves in the position of making a living creature of the biological unit itself. We should thus approach the views of those, like Kubiëna,[4] who regard the earth itself as a living creature of superior rank. Uexküll (1920) did not associate the lifeless elements of an environment in his idea of a total order. He confined its extent to the living elements. We

[4] 1948.

are thus not far removed from the views of a number of sociologists and political economists.

In his *Decline of the West,* Spengler (1918) described civilizations as living beings which grow up "with the same sublime lack of purpose as the flowers of the field". Similarly Othmar Spann (1939) regarded human beings as members of a greater whole. We must now ask ourselves if our definition of wholeness permits of such an extension. The characteristic we thought fundamental to the living whole was, along with purposiveness, an order making for wholeness, a relating of parts together. We can undoubtedly see such a relation of the parts in the members of a social community or in the members of an ecological unit. But is this an order making for wholeness? We said that the fish belonged to the water, the humble bee to the dead nettle; but we shall soon see that, while there is in these cases a correlation, there is no order which could be thought of as constituting a whole. If I find a beetle's leg, this leg is, so to speak, nothing, because I can describe it only as a fragment of the whole beetle. The leg has no independence; it could not come into existence on its own; it is but a member. If I broke it off a beetle I should be tearing it out of the order in which it belonged. It would have become dead and rigid. Its form alone would remind me of its origin and purpose. If we examine a fish its whole organization reminds us of the water. But it is not the member of some body, a part of the pond from which it has been taken. It is possible with absolute certainty to deduce the existence of a whole beetle from a single leg. But a paradise fish does not provide me with sufficient data to deduce the existence of some Chinese pool; it can also come into the world in an aquarium and flourish wonderfully there. One member of an ecological community is not a part isolated by logical abstraction or dissection; it is a unit, and in its unitary wholeness, in its individuality it exhibits but one ordered relationship; this is the one that places it in a definite relationship to other things, to similar isolated organisms. The healthy paradise fish in the aquarium finds there everything which he would have found in a Chinese pond. The certainty born of our experience of regularity, therefore, relates the members of an organism to the organism as a whole, but it does not relate the organism to its biotope as though that were a whole; the organism is placed rather in an ordered relationship, as a unit, to the nature to which it belongs. There is therefore nothing more than a co-ordination of individuals. *It is apparent then that co-ordination can produce wholeness, but co-ordination can also be clearly recognized where it does not constitute a whole.*

5. "FORMA CORPORIS" AS FINAL CAUSE

Driesch went out of his way to avoid using the concept of purposiveness in his description of the life process. I, on the other hand, have deliberately emphasized it in every detail of our study and have tried to prove its existence. Every living process has an end in view.

Even if we were to choose some other expression instead of purposiveness, it also must be derived from our human conceptual thought. If we spoke of something as happening "fortuitously" we should still be employing a term drawn from our own experience. We call that part of our behaviour which is deliberate, "purposive", and that which happens unintentionally and without the co-operation of any other person, "fortuitous". The charge of anthropomorphism applies as much and as little to the one expression as to the other. We have deliberately made use of all the different expressions which denote a teleological principle, and which are accepted by many authors. Other expressions with similar meanings are sometimes rejected. Our own views are best expressed by Gustav Wolff's (1935) term *zielursachlich* which implies that the end striven after is the cause of the process. The views expressed in the various parts of this book may be summed up as follows:

1. All the separate parts of chemical processes lead to a particular goal. While the co-ordination of each chemical reaction depends upon the elementary potentialities of the atoms, the way in which these reactions follow one another

leads to a definite goal, which would never be attained, were the atomic forces left to their own devices. This fact becomes all the clearer in the light of the fact that the same end is reached by very different chemical means. One process can take the place of another; protein combustion can replace sugar combustion; chemosynthesis can replace photosynthesis.

2. Morphogenetic processes are subject to a similar central control. We saw how *Stentor* regenerated parts that were lacking, and how the balance between nucleus and cytoplasm was restored when it was disturbed. The nucleus-cytoplasm relationship is by itself only a partial end which is attained by the morphogenetic processes of the cell. Half an egg leads to the same result as a complete egg, though the result is on a smaller scale. Haploid eggs have to make more divisions than the diploid eggs to result in the complete *Pluteus* larva. Here is another obvious case of the end determining the course taken.

3. Adaptation and capacity to react are directed in such a way that they are bound to result in the organism's living harmoniously in its environment. This result is achieved once more through the end in view acting causally upon the given material conditions.

It could, of course, be objected that none of this justifies us in setting life in a special category. Hydrogen and oxygen lead to water, sodium and chlorine to common salt. Hence water and salt are the goals to which these processes are directed. Gustav Wolff[5] has pointed out the difference. The "mill" of a glacier leads to the production of rounded stones. Similar stones could be produced in a mill-like machine. Yet in the milling of the glacier there is no purposive natural phenomenon. Let us apply the analogy to water and common salt. Sodium and chlorine produce common salt. Hydrogen and chlorine yield hydrochloric acid. In neither case is the end-product a goal; it is a result. Hydrogen and chlorine have certain properties and so hydrochloric acid develops from them, and the reactions of hydrochloric acid depend upon the

[5] 1933, 1935.

molecules with which it makes contact. A stable condition is always the result, as I have shown. But this stable condition is not a thing aimed at. The antecedent, more unstable, condition cannot be maintained in opposition to the possible stable one, "so that" a change ensues, which can be anticipated on the basis of our experience of regularity. This "so that" characterizes the changes occurring in the inanimate sphere. In the sphere of life, on the other hand, we are obliged to say that sugar or protein are burnt-up "in order that" the energy necessary for life may be liberated. The opposition between "so that" and "in order that" reveals the difference between the necessary occurrence of a result and the purposively conditioned vital phenomenon. There we have the fundamental contrast between living and non-living processes.

The concept of wholeness cannot be regarded as applicable only to life, for there are wholes in the inanimate sphere too. Wholeness, in so far as it signifies something composite, is just what we find in inanimate matter. If we employ the terminology of traditional philosophy and try to describe the *forma* of a molecule, we shall have to say that the *forma corporis* of a molecule consists in the relationship among its atoms, and that of the atom, in the relationship between the nuclear components and the electrons. It is this ordered relationship which makes the parts into a whole.

But is a living organism a whole in this sense? Driesch's half egg was not complete, and yet a complete sea-urchin emerged from it. A haploid egg is not a whole; it has not its full quota of chromosomes. In spite of this it produced a complete *Proteus*. According to Driesch (1928), a whole no longer remains a whole when it lacks a part; a plate, e.g., is not a whole when a piece of it is broken off. Driesch broke off half an egg, Boveri (1910) some of the chromosomes from an ovum-nucleus, yet both fragments developed into what one would call living wholes. *In inanimate matter wholeness is not wholeness if a part is missing; in the sphere of life, on the other hand, wholeness implies a striving for wholeness even when something is lacking.*

The wholeness of a living being, therefore, is a goal which is aimed at. It is unthinkable and inexplicable without end-causality. Gustav Wolff (1935) saw the fundamental defect in Driesch's definition. Is a dog whole when three of its hairs have been cut off? Is it whole when a foot or four legs have been amputated? If wholeness is the presence of all the parts, certainly not. The living organism then, is not a whole in so far as it is a composition of parts; it is a whole to the extent that parts are directed to the end of forming together a whole. Wholeness is, as it were, a degree of perfection, aimed at continually, but never fully attained, for every organism lacks something, every organism is in some way damaged. To the extent that this harmonious wholeness is the cause and the end of every separate process, the criterion of the organism's existence is this wholeness produced by end-causality. In other words: *The form of the living body as space- and time-form is the goal to which all the phenomena of life are directed.*

6. "ORDO NATURAE" AS END-CAUSALITY

When I remarked above that *forma corporis* of the living organism, as a space and time form, is a goal or end which acts simultaneously as a cause, I might have inferred that an environment with its harmonious interrelation of its many living inhabitants is a goal or end of the same sort. A disturbance in the living space is immediately evened out just as one is evened out within an organism. The harmony of a biotope must in this case be as much an end-cause as the harmony of an organism is; the biotope too, will have a space- and time-form. Earlier on we firmly rejected the idea of wholeness as applicable to the living space. There is an ordered system, it is true, but it is merogenous. The correlation which brings about this order rests upon the separate members of the biotope, which are, therefore, not the members of a whole but merely members of a multiple living community. Gustav Wolff (1935) made a very fine distinction between the "acervus", the unordered pile, in which it does not matter what position the separate constituents occupy, and the "cumulus", in which it matters enormously whether one part is at the top or the bottom of the pile. A living space, a living community is a cumulus of this sort. All the living spaces on earth are related one to the other and to the inanimate factors within them, no less than to the living ones. Thus, in the long run, one can regard the whole earth as an accumulation of large numbers of cumuli. But we have at the same time established that this accumulation is a merogenously constituted system, because the potentialities which lead to the interrelation of the living creatures are immanent in individual living organisms.

Nevertheless we shall have to admit that the above statement, though essentially correct, is in certain respects incomplete. If it is true, however, the concept of end-causality would not apply to this accumulation; we should have here only a pseudo-teleology. The living beings have every possible characteristic so that this accumulation ensues, but not in order that this accumulation may ensue. It is, therefore, an order *post rem*. Erich Becher,[6] however, managed to prove that galls in plants bear the relationship of organs to the wasps which harbour their offspring in them. Among the various species the plant-gall has varying degrees of development and perfection. Hence the plant has the potentiality to realize something which cannot possibly serve its own ends. The gall-forming plant serves the end of the insect in a way which cannot possibly serve its own ends. The plant is so constructed that it can and must serve the insect. Here, therefore, an ordered relationship is brought about which has nothing to do with that immanent purposiveness of which we spoke, since it goes far beyond this in serving another organism. Where shall we find the springs of this merogenous interrelation? The plant produces in the interests of the wasps a first-class organ for rearing their brood. Is there any advantage to the plant in so doing? Does it even partially help to maintain or improve the species? Without this ability of the plants to produce galls, the wasps' adaptation to this sort of brood-care is meaningless, or at least inexplicable. No purely merogenous correlation

[6] 1925, 1926.

could possibly explain the wasp's adaptation to the gall-forming plant, or, on the other hand, the plant's adaptation to the wasp.

The phenomena of convergence point in the same direction. The tree-frog provides a good example. The required conditions are trees with insects living on them. A frog, possessing as a climbing device feet with adhesive pads and a tongue which it can shoot out, should theoretically be able to find its nourishment here. Now does this possibility actually induce the development of frogs that fulfil these conditions? Throughout most of the world this type of life is represented by the Hylae (the true tree-frogs) which have thus occupied the "plot" on the plan (to use Kühnelt's term). That this is a phylogenetic adaptation appears from the fact that the tree-frogs are descendants of ground dwellers such as *Chlorophilus* or *Acris*, which, apart from their not being adapted to a tree existence, are thoroughgoing "Hylae".

Adaptation to life in the trees started from an ancestral form of this sort. In South-east Asia there are no genuine Hylidae. The chance of living in the manner of a tree-frog exists there all the same and the opportunity offered is seized. The "plot" is occupied in this region by the genus *Racophorus* which is clearly descended from the Ranidae (the true water-frogs). Whether it is the tree with the opportunities it offers which induces an adaptation to tree life, or whether the Ranidae have in them the potentiality of producing tree-frogs phylogenetically, the question still remains: Why do the Ranidae develop into tree-frogs only in places where there are no Hylae? The initiative cannot be sought in the tree or the non-arboreal Ranidae or even in both conjointly. There are trees and Ranidae everywhere, so that the development ought to occur everywhere, too. The fact that this particular "plot" is only occupied by Ranidae when it is left vacant by the Hylidae, proves that the driving forces in the ordered relationship cannot be attributed to the merogenous members of the biotope. It is even possible to prove an individual, mutual substitution as between two species; this occurs in the relationship between grass- and water-frogs in the European area. In the spring, in the various pools, we find either water- or grass-frogs laying their eggs. But while the water-frogs spend the whole summer in or near the water, the grass-frogs soon leave the water and live on land right up to the autumn. In mountainous regions water-frogs cannot survive owing to the slow development of their tadpoles and the shortness of the summer. But grass-frogs can. During the summer, therefore, the ponds might well offer possibilities of life which are not exploited by frogs, and these opportunities might well pass unnoticed. This, however, is not the case; throughout the summer a number of grass-frogs remain in the water leading the life of water-frogs, while others lead a grass-frog existence on land. The opportunity which appeared neglected is in fact utilized to the full. Why is it that in districts where water-frogs are found. grass-frogs never live in the same way as do grass-frogs in mountainous regions? Is it perhaps because this "plot" is already occupied? This certainly appears to be the case. But what is the origin of this principle? How does it bring about the practical utilization of each separate possibility of life? Surely one is not justified in assuming that this principle is immanent in all those forms which are capable of replacing one another? Thus we see even here a harmony achieved, in which the end acts causally, a harmony, however, which cannot be immanent in the individual constituents as such. This applies to all the examples I have selected—the plant galls, the frog genera which replace one another, and even individual organisms.

We are, therefore, obliged to recognize a principle of ordered relationship in all life processes, which extends beyond the living individual.

The explanation I have attempted in these pages leads to the conclusion, therefore, that the harmony to which the individual is subordinate is again an end to which separate processes—in this case, the lives of individuals—are co-ordinated. This harmony, too, is an end which operates causally. It is the pre-established harmony of nature.

FINIS CORONAT OPUS

16+

BIBLIOGRAPHY

ABEL, 1912. *Paläobiologie*, Stuttgart.

ALTMANN, 1890–94. *Die Elementarorganismen und ihre Beziehungen zu den Zellen*, Leipzig.

ALVERDES, 1936. *Leben als Sinnverwirklichung.*

—— 1940. *Die Stellung der Biologie innerhalb der Wissenschaften.*

ANDRE, 1931. *Urbild und Ursache in der Biologie*, München.

—— 1947. Philosophie der Blüte, Zeitschrift "Die Begegnung".

ANDREP, 1927. *Conditioned Reflexes*, trans. from Pavlov, Oxford.

BACON, 1605. *The Advancement of Learning*, London.

BALBIANI, 1888. "Recherches expérimentales sur la mérotomie des Infusoires ciliés." *Rev. Zool. Suise*, **5**; and 1892, *Ann. de Micrographie*, **4**.

BAVINK, 1927–29. *Hauptfragen der heutigen Naturphilosophie*, Berlin.

—— 1954. *Ergebnisse und Probleme der Naturwissenschaften.* 10th ed. with Aloys Wenzl, Schubert-Soldern, W. Gerlach, Zürich. 1st ed., 1913.

BECHER, 1925. "Erkenntnistheorie und Metaphysik", in *Philosophie in Einzeldarstellungen von Desoir*, Berlin.

—— 1926. *Einführung in die Philosophie*, München.

BECKER, 1926. "The role of the nucleus in the cell functions of *Amoeba*." *Biol. Bull.*, **50**.

BELAR, 1926a. "Der Formenwechsel der Protistenkerne." *Ergebnisse und Fortschr., Zoologie*, **6**.

—— 1926b. "Zur Cytologie von *Aggregata eberthi*." *Arch. Protist.*, **53**.

—— 1928. *Die cytologischen Grundlagen der Vererbung.* Handbuch der Vererbungswissenschaften.

BERGSON, 1920. *Einführung in die Metaphysik.*

—— 1921. *Schöpferische Entwicklung*, original ed. 1907.

BERTALANFFY, 1932. *Theoretische Biologie*, Berlin.

—— 1949. *Biologisches Weltbild*, Bern.

BETHE, 1931. "Plastizität und Zentrenlehre." *Handb. f. norm. Path. physiol.*, **15**.

BIERENS DE HAAN, 1940. *Die tierischen Instinkte und ihr Umbau durch Erfahrung*, Leiden.

BOVERI, 1899. *Die Entwicklung von Ascaris megalocephala mit besonderer Rücksicht auf die Kernverhältnisse,* Jena.

—— 1901. "Ueber die Polarität des Seeigeleies." *Verh. Phys.-Med. Ges.* Würzburg, **34.**

—— 1901. "Die Polarität von Ovocyte, Ei und Larve des *Stronglyocentrotus lividus.*" *Zool. Jahr. Abt. Anat. u. Ontog.,* **14.**

—— 1904. *Ergebnisse über die Konstitution der chromatischen Kernsubstanz,* Jena.

—— 1905. "Ueber die Abhängigkeit der Kerngrösse und Zellenzahl der Seeigellarven von der Chromosomenzahl der Ausgangszellen." *Zellstudien,* **5.**

—— 1910. "Ueber die Teilung zentrifugierter Eier von *Ascaris megalocephala.*" *Arch. Entwmech. Org.,* **30.**

—— 1910. "Die Potenzen der *Ascaris*-Blastomeren bei abgeänderter Furchung. Zugleich ein Beitrag zur Frage qualitativ ungleicher Chromosomenteilungen." *Fetschr. 60. Geburtstag von R. Hertwig,* **3,** Jena.

BOYSEN-JENSEN, 1939. *Pflanzenphysiologie,* Jena.

BURKAMP, 1929. *Die Struktur der Ganzheiten,* Berlin.

CARMICHAEL, 1926. "The development of behaviour in vertebrates experimentally removed from the influence of external stimulation." *Psychol. Rev.,* **33.**

CHILD, 1924. *Physiological Foundations of Behaviour,* New York.

CONRAD-MARTIUS, 1944. *Selbstaufbau der Natur,* Hamburg.

DARWIN, 1859. *Die Entstehung der Arten.*

DRIESCH, 1891–92. "Entwicklungsphysiologische Studien 1–6." *Z. wiss. Zool.,* **53** and **55.**

—— 1893a. "Entwicklungsphysiologische Studien 7–10." *Mitt. Zool. Stat. Neapel,* 1893.

—— 1893b. "Zur Theorie der organischen Formbildung." *Biol. Zbl.,* **13.**

—— 1895. *Analytische Theorie der organischen Entwicklung,* Leipzig.

—— 1928a. *Philosophie des Organischen,* 4th ed. 1938, Leipzig.

—— 1928b. *Der Mensch und die Welt,* Leipzig.

—— 1935. *Ueberwindung des Materialismus,* Zürich.

—— 1941. "Biologische Probleme höherer Ordnung." *Bios,* Leipzig.

DUJARDIN, 1841. See Nowikoff, *Grundzüge der Geschichte der biologischen Theorien,* 1949, München.

DÜRKEN, 1925a. "Das Verhalten embryonaler Zellen im Interplantat." *Zool. Anz. Erg.,* **1.**

—— 1925b. *Hauptprobleme der Biologie,* München.

EHRENBERG, 1938. *Die Infusorientierchen als vollkommene Organismen.* See Nowikoff, 1949.

FABRE, 1879. *Souvenirs entomologiques. Etudes sur l'instinct,* Paris, Series 1–10, 1879–1910.

FISCHER, 1901. Cited from F. and M. Fieser, *Lehrbuch der organischen Chemie,* 2, Verlag Chemie, Weinheim/Bergstrasse, 1955.

FRISCH, 1915. "Der Farbensinn und Formensinn der Bienen." *Zool. Jarhb. Physiol.,* 35.

GABRIEL, 1949a. *Vom Brahma zur Existenz,* Wien.

—— 1949b. *Logik der Weltanschauung,* Graz.

GIERSBERG, 1922. "Untersuchungen über den Plasmabau der Amöben im Hinblick auf die Wabentheorie." *Arch. Entwmech. Org.,* 51.

GREDT, 1946. *Elementa philosophiae,* Freiberg.

GRUBER, 1885. Cited from Przibram: *Einleitung in die Experimentelle Morphologie der Tiere,* Leipzig and Wein.

GUILLERMOND, 1914. "État actuel de la question de l'evolution et du rôle physiologique des mitochondries." *Rev. Gen.,* 26.

GURWITSCH, 1923. *Versuch einer synthetischen Biologie,* Berlin.

—— 1927. "Weiterbildung und Verallgemeinerung des Feldbegriffes." *Arch. Entwmech. Org.,* 112.

—— 1930. *Die histologischen Grundlagen der Biologie,* Jena.

HAECKEL, 1866. *Generelle Morphologische der Organismen.* Berlin, Neudruck, 1906.

HARTMANN, M., 1932. *Allgemeine Biologie, ihre Aufgaben, ihr gegenwärtiger Stand und ihre Methode,* Jena.

—— 1933. *Allgemeine Biologie,* Jena, 4th ed. Stuttgart, 1953.

HARTMANN, N., 1940. Der Aufbau der realen Welt (Grundriss der allgemeinen Kategorienlehre).

HEINTEL, 1944a. "Das Innere der Natur", in *Wissenschaft und Weltbild,* 3.

—— 1944b. "Der 'Wiener Kries' und die Dialektik der Erfahrung", from *Philosophie der Wirklichkeitsnähe,* Festschrift R. Reininger, Wien.

HERBST, 1893. "Experimentelle Untersuchungen über den Einfluss der veränderten chemischen Zusammensetzung des umgebenden Mediums auf die Entwicklung der Tiere." *Z. wiss. Zool.,* 55.

HERTWIG, O., 1875–78. "Beiträge zur Kenntnis der Bildung, Befruchtung und Teilung des tierschen Eies, 1–4." *Morph. Jb.*, **1, 3** and **4**.

—— 1897. *Mechanik und Biologie*, Jena.

—— 1916. *Vom Werden der Organismen*, Jena.

—— 1921. *Allgemeine Biologie*, Jena.

HERTWIG, R., 1902. "Protozoen und die Zelltheorie." *Arch. f. Protist.*, **1**.

HERTZ, 1929–31. "Die Organisation des optischen Feldes bei der Biene, 1–3." *Z. f. vergl. Physiol.*, **8**, 1929a; **11**, 1929b; **14**, 1931.

—— 1936. "Beitrag zum Farben- und Formsehen der Bienen." *Z. f. vergl. Physiol.*, **24**.

—— 1937. "Zur Technik und Methodik der Bienenversuche mit Farbpapieren und Glasfiltern." *Z. f. vergl. Physiol.*, **25**.

HESSE, 1935. *Tierbau und Tierleben in ihren Zusammenhang betrachtet*, 1st ed. 1935; 2nd 1943, Jena.

HOERSTADIUS, 1935. "Ueber die Determination im Verlauf der Eiachse bei Seeigeln." *Public Staz. Zool. Napol.*, **14**.

HOFER, 1890. "Experimentelle Untersuchungen über den Einfluss des Kerns auf das Protoplasma." *Jena Z. Naturw.*, **24**.

HOLTFRETER, 1934. "Ueber die Verbreitung induzierender Substanzen und ihre Leistungen im Tritonkeim." *Arch. Entwmech. Org.*, **132**.

HUME, 1748. *Untersuchungen über den menschlichen Verstand.*

HUZELLA, 1941. *Zwischenzellige Organisation als Grundlage der Interzellulartheorie und Interzellularpathologie*, Berlin.

JOHNSON, 1893. "A contribution to the morphology and biology of the Stentors." *J. Morph.*, **8**.

JORDAN, 1935. *Physikalisches Denken in der neuen Zeit.*

—— 1949. *Die Physik des 20. Jahrhunderts.*

KANT, I. *Critique of Reason. Critique of Teleological Judgment, Critique of Judgment.* Trans. J. H. Bernard, 1914, London.

KEKULÉ, 1859. From Fieser and Fieser: *Lehrbuch der organischen Chemie*, Weinheim/Bergstrasse, 1955.

KOEHLER, O., 1932–33. "Biologie und Ganzheitsproblem", in *Der Biologie*, **2**, H. 15.

—— 1949. "Die Analyse der Taxisanteile instinktartigen Verhaltens." *Soc. exp. Biol. Symp.*, **4**.

KÖHLER, W., 1921. *Intelligenzprüfungen bei Menschenaffen*, Berlin.

—— 1929. *Gestalt-Psychology*, New York.

KOSSEL, 1946. In P. Eskola: *Kristalle und Gesteine*, Wien.

KREIDL, 1904. "Weitere Beiträge zur Physiologe des Ohrlabyrinths." *Arch. ges. Physiol.*, **103**.

KUBIËNA, 1948. *Entwicklungslehre des Bodens*, Wien.

KÜHN, 1941. *Grundriss der allgemeinen Zoologie*, Leipzig. 13th ed. Stuttgart, 1959.

—— 1955. *Entwicklungsphysiologie*, Berlin, Göttingen, Heidelberg.

KÜHNELT, 1943. Die Leitformenmethode in der Oekologie der Landtiere.

—— 1948. "Ein Beitrag zur Kenntnis der Bodentierwelt einiger Waldtypen Kärntens." *Carinthia*, Klagenfurt.

—— 1950. *Bodenbiologie*, Wien.

LAMARCK, 1809. *Philosophie Zoölogique*, trans. H. Elliott, 1914, London.

LENARD, 1937. *Grosse Naturforscher*, **3**.

LEWIS, 1916. In P. Eskola: *Kristalle und Gesteine*, 1946, Wien.

LILLIE, 1896. On the smallest parts of Stentor capable of regeneration. *J. Morph.*, **12**.

—— 1929. "Embryonic segregation and its role in the life history." *Arch. Entwmech. Org.*, **118**.

LINSER, 1948. *Chemismus des Lebens*, Wien.

LORENZ, 1931. "Beiträge zur Ethologie sozialer Corviden." *J. Ornithol.*, **79**.

—— 1935. "Der Kumpan in der Umwelt des Vogels." *J. Ornith.*, **83**.

—— 1937a. "Ueber die Bildung des Instinktbegriffes." *Naturwisschaft.*, **25**.

—— 1937b. "Ueber den Begriff der Instinkthandlung." *Fol. Biotheoret.*, **2**.

—— 1941. "Vergleichende Verhaltensforschung." *Zool. Anz.*, **12**.

—— 1943. "Die angeborenen Formen möglicher Erfahrung." *Z. Tierpsychol.*, **5**.

MANGOLD, H., 1929. "Organisatorentransplantationen in verscheidenen Kombinationen bei Urodelen." *Arch. Entwmech. Org.*, **117**.

MANGOLD, H., 1927. "Ueber formative Reizung in der Entwicklung der Amphibien." *Naturwisschaft.*, **14**.

—— 1929. "Das Determinationsproblem." *Ergeb. Biol.*, **3**.

MARCH, 1948. *Natur und Erkenntniss*, Wien.

MEYER-ABICH, 1948. *Naturphilosophie auf neuen Wegen*, Stuttgart.

MITTASCH, 1938. *Katalyse und Determinismus*.

MITTERER, 1947. *Die Zeugung der Organismen, insbesondere des Menschen*, Wien.

MOEWUS, 1939. "Untersuchungen über die relative Sexualität von Algen." *Biol. Zbl.*, **59**.

—— 1951. *Die Sexualstoffe von Chlamydomonas eugametos. Ergeb. Enzymf.*, **12**.

MORGAN, C. L., 1912. *Instinct and Experience*.

—— 1923. *A Philosophy of Evolution*.

MORGAN, T. H., 1913. *Heredity and Sex*, New York.

—— 1921. *Die stofflichen Grundlage der Vererbung*, Berlin.

MOYSE, 1948. *Biologie et Physico-Chemie*, Paris.

NÄGELI, 1862. "Proteinkristalloide." *S.B. bayer. Akad. Wiss.*

—— 1928. *Micellartheorie*. Nachdruck in Oswalds Klassikern der exakten Wissenschaften, Leipzig.

NEUBERG, 1944. *Das naturwissenschaftliche Weltbild der Gegenwart.* Göttingen.

NOWIKOFF, 1949. *Grundzüge der Geschichte der biologischen Theorien*, München.

NUSSBAUM, 1886. Ueber die Teilbarkeit der lebenden Materia. 1. *Bonn. Arch. mikr. Anat.*, **26**.

PASCHER, 1914. *Flagellaten*, Jena.

—— 1918. "Von einer allen Algenreihen gemeinsamen Entwicklungsregel." *Verh. Deutsch. Bot. Ges.*, **36**.

PASTEUR, 1862. *Ann. Chim. Phys.* Ser. 3, **64**.

PAVLOV, 1926. *Die höchste Nervenstätigkeit (das Verhalten) von Tieren*, München.

—— 1932. *Vorlesungen über die Arbeit der Grosshirnhemisphären*, Leningrad.

PFLUGER, 1875. "Ueber die physiologische Verbrennung in den lebenden Organismen." *Arch. Ges. Physiol.*, **10**.

PIEKARSKI, 1937. *Arch. f. Mikrobiol.*

PLATE, 1924. *Allg. Zool. Abstamm. Jena.*

PORTMANN, 1944. *Biologische Fragmente zu einer Lehre vom Menschen*, Bern.

—— 1946. *Die Tiergestalt.*

PREYER, 1880. "Die hypothesen über den Ursprung des Lebens", in *Naturwissenschaftliche Tatsachen und Probleme*, Berlin.

PROVAZEK, 1895–97. "Beiträge zur Kenntnis der Rhizopoden." *Z. wiss. Zool.*, **61**.

—— 1903. "Beitrag zur Kenntnis der Regeneration und Biologie der Protozoen." *Arch. f. Protist.*, **3**.

REICHENOW, 1928. "Ergebnisse mit der Nuklealfärbung bei Protozoen." *Arch. f. Protist.*, **61**.

RICHTER, 1865. "Zur Darwinschen Lehre." *Schmids Jahrb. ges. Med.,* **126** and 1870, **148**.

RICKERT, 1921. *Die Grenzen der naturwissenschaftlichen Begriffsbildung,* Tübingen.

RIEHL, 1908. *"Logic und Erkenntnistheorie"* in *Kultur der Gengenwart:* Syst. Philosophie, **2**, Berlin and Leipzig.

ROHRACHER, 1947. *Einführung in die Psychologie,* Wien, 6th ed. 1958.

ROUX, 1893. *Die Bedeutung der Kernteilungsfiguren,* Leipzig.

SCHAFFER, 1933. *Lehrbuch der Histologie und Histogenese,* Berlin.

SCHLEIDEN, 1833. "Beiträge zur Phytogenesis", in Muller's *Archiv.*

SCHLICK, 1918. *Allgemeine Erkenntnislehre,* Berlin.

—— 1925. "Naturphilosophie", in *Philosophie in ihren Einzelgebieten,* Desoir, Berlin.

SCHRÖDINGER, 1947. *Was ist Leben?* Bern.

SCHUBERT-SOLDERN, 1947. *Die Abstammungslehre,* Wien.

SCHWANN, 1839. *Mikroskopische Untersuchungen über die Uebereinstimmung in der Struktur und im Wachstum der Tiere und Pflanzen,* Berlin.

SIEBOLD, 1845. See Nowikoff, 1949.

SOCHOLOFF, 1924. "Das Regenerationsproblem bei Protozoen." *Arch. f. Protist.,* **47**.

SPANN, 1939. *Kategorienlehre,* **2**.

SPEMANN, 1936. *Experimentelle Beiträge zur einer Theorie der Entwicklung,* Berlin.

SPENCER, 1893. "A Rejoinder to Professor Weismann." *Contemp. Rev.,* **64**.

SPENGLER, 1918. *Der Untergang des Abendlandes,* Band 1, Gestalt und Wirklichkeit.

STOLTE, 1922. "Der Einfluss der Umwelt auf Makronukleus und Plasma von *Stentor coeruleus* Ehrenberg." *Arch. f. Protist.,* **45**.

STORCH, 1948. *Die Sonderstellung des Menschen in Lebensabspiel und Vererbung,* Wien.

—— 1949. "Erbmotorik und Erwerbmotorik." *S.B. Oesterr. Akad. Wiss.*

TIMOFEEFF-RESSOVSKY, 1937. *Experimentelle Mutationsforschung in der Vererbungslehre,* Dresden.

—— 1940. "Eine biophysikalische Analyse des Mutationsvorganges." *Nova Acta Leopoldina,* N.F. **9**.

UEXKÜLL, 1920. *Theoretische Biologie*, Berlin.

—— 1921. *Umwelt und Innenwelt der Tiere*, Berlin.

—— 1935. "Die Bedeutung der Umweltforschung für die Erkenntnis des Lebens." *Z. ges. Naturwiss.*, 1.

UNGERER, 1941. "Die Erkenntnisgrundlagen der Biologie", in *Handbuch der Biologie*, 1, Berlin.

VERWORN, 1888. "Biologische Protistenkunde." *Z. wiss. Zool.*, 47.

—— 1890. *Psychophysiologische Protistenkunde*, Jena.

—— 1891. "Die physiologische Bedeutung des Zellkerns." *Arch. ges. Physiol.*, 51.

—— 1915. *Allgemeine Physiologie*, Jena.

VOGT, 1923. "Morphologische und physiologische Fragen der Primitiventwicklung, *Sitzungsber. Ges. Morph. Physiol.*, München, 35.

WARBURG, 1921. *Physiologische Chemie der Zellatmung*. Berlin.

—— 1928. "Ueber die chemische Konstitution des Atmungsfermentes." *Naturwisschaft.*, 16.

—— 1932. "Das Sauerstoff übertragende Ferment der Atmungsfermentes." *Ang. Chemie*, 45.

WEINLAND, 1901. "Ueber Kohlehydratzersetzung ohne Sauerstoffzufuhr bei *Ascaris*." *Z. Biol.*, 42.

WEISMANN, 1892. *Das Keimplasma*, Jena.

—— 1902. *Vorträge über Deszendenztheorie*, Jena.

WEISS, 1924. "Entwicklungsmechanik, Regeneration, Transplantation", *Johrb. Ges. Physiol.*, 3.

—— 1926. "Morphodynamik", *Abh. theor. Biol. H.*, 23.

WENZL, 1930. "Der Gestalt und Ganzheitsbegriff in der modernen Psychologie, Biologie und Philosophie und sein Verhältnis zum Entelechiebegriff", in *Philosophia Perennis*, Regensburg.

—— 1936. *Wissenschaft und Weltanschauung*, Leipzig.

—— 1938. *Metaphysik und Physik von heute*, Leipzig.

WILSON, 1925. *The Cell in Development and Heredity*, 3rd ed., New York.

WINOGRADSKY, 1922. In *Zbl. f. Bacteriol.*, 57.

WÖHLER, 1828. "Ueber künstliche Bildung des Harnstoffes." *Poggendorfs Ann. Phys. Chemie*, 12.

WOLFF, 1933. *Leben und Erkennen*, München.

—— 1935. "Das Problem des Vitalismus." *Die medizinische Welt*, 9.

WOLTERECK, 1940. *Ontologie des Lebendigen*, Stuttgart.

ZIEGLER, 1920. *Der Begriff des Instinktes einst und jetzt*, Jena.

ZUMSTEIN, 1900. "Zur Morphologie und Physiologie von *Euglena gracilis*," Pringsheim, *Jahrb.*, Bd. 34.

INDEX

Abel, O., 162, 170
Abstraction, 2, 3, 4, 7, 8, 158, 218
Acetabularia, 101
Acytaria, 93
Adaptation, 9, 173, 226
  and purposiveness, 209
  and reactivity, 149–74, 210, 222
  ecological, 153–61
  expression of form, 162–64, 171–4
  fundamental, 161, 164, 172, 173
  morphological and function, 162–3
  planned, 212
Adrenal cortex, 183
Agnosticism, 68
  nominalist, 10
Albumin, 25
Algae (*and see* Blue-green algae), 118, 145
Altmann, 52, 93
Alverdes, 187
Amoeba, 101, 176
  diploidea, 96
Amphibia, 91, 189
Andre, 12
Andrep, 194
Anfangsorganisation, 110
Antirrhinum majus, 104
"Anthropopsychologism", 151
Ape, 202, 205
Appetence behaviour, 202, 205
Aquinas, Thomas, 12
Aristotle, xii, xiii, 6, 15, 20, 66, 67, 113
  and active principle, 113
  and hylomorphism, 11–13
Asclepiadaceae, 157, 163
Aspergillus niger, 53
Atomism, genetic, 106
Auxin, 179–83
Atoms, 13, 14, 15, 19, 23, 25, 28, 33, 35, 36, 37, 38, 39, 40, 44, 66, 67, 70, 141, 142, 210, 213, 218
  structure of, 40–3

Bacon, Francis, xii
Bacteria, 29, 55, 93, 95, 96, 99
Bacteriophage (phage), 94
Bavink, 14
Becher, E., 3, 225
Beer, G. de, 89
Beetle, 149, 150, 154, 210, 220
Begonia, 125, 138, 139, 140
Behaviour, 152, 153, 195, 203, 189, 190, 196, 198, 202, 208
  appetence, 202, 205
  patterns, 193
Bergson, H., 171
Bertalanffy, L. von, 18, 19, 20, 33, 60, 61, 116, 141
Bierens de Haan, 171, 187, 195, 198
Biochemistry, 21, 68
  and epistemology, 1–45
Biogen, Verworn's, 52, 58, 93
Biogenesis, Hertwig's theory of, 79
Biologische Probleme höherer Ordnung, Driesch's, 31
Biotope (*and see* Environment), 131, 136, 154, 155, 156, 157, 221, 224
Biotype, 117, 163, 204
Birds, 188, 189, 191, 192, 196–7, 198, 199, 208
  of paradise, 160
Blastomere, 79, 80, 81, 89, 130
Blepharoplasts, 100
Blue-green algae, 93, 95, 96, 98, 99, 101
Boveri, 74, 86, 132, 135, 223
  experiments with sea-urchin eggs, 132–3
  gradient theory of, 89–90
Boysen-Jensen, 139
Burkamp, 216
Buzzard, 192

Cacti, 157
Callus, in *Nicotiana*, 139, 140
Carmichael, 189
Carotin, 98, 177, 180

Casparsson, 96
Catabolism, 53
Cause (causality), 3, 4, 6, 12, 30, 39, 63, 66, 68, 70, 113, 170, 212
  end, as *ordo naturae*, 224–7
  factors, 150
  final, and *forma corporis*, 221–4
  goal, in sponge, 137–8
  order, 149–53
Cell, the, 9, 25, 26, 74, 75, 76, 91, 92, 93, 96, 97, 98, 108, 110, 114, 120, 141, 175, 180, 208, 209, 218
  entelechy, 115
  and form, 109, 126–32
  and molecules, order, 142–3
  and nucleus, 99
  and potentialities, 82, 83, 123–6, 132
  and space-form, 113
  and time-form, 113, 114, 122
  and viruses, 94–5
  as prototype of hologenous system, 113
  as unit of living form, 91–6
  as whole, 108, 109
  conception of, abstract, 109–10
  cleavage of egg, 101
  division (mitosis), 76, 78, 79, 97, 98, 106, 110, 114, 115, 116, 126, 127, 128, 129, 130
  development of egg and protist compared, 126–7
  developmental potentialities of, 123–6, 135
  egg (ovum), 76, 77, 79, 80, 82, 83, 84, 92, 101, 121, 126, 222
  experimental work on eggs, 80, 89–90, 132–3
  experiments on *Stentor*, 111–12
  individuality of, 91–115
  meristematic, 83, 138, 139
  nature of, in relation to position, 122
  no correspondence of protist with metabiont, 145
  of metabiont and protist homologous, 126
  omnipotentiality of egg, 73
  physical unit of life, 25–6, 91
  polarity of, 89, 101, 112
  relation of protist to metabiont, 116–26

  significance of in metabiont, 136
  size and gastrulation, 133
  sociability of, 126–7
  somatic, 74–5
  subordination of, 145
  unity of, 112, 120–1
Centriole, 98, 100
Centrosome, 97, 98, 101, 116
Child, gradient theory of, 89–90
Chladozeres, 172
Chloroplasts, 98, 157
Chromatin, 75, 99, 100
Chromoplasts, 98
Chromosomes, 76, 77, 97, 99, 106
  and genes, 103–7
  deletion, 107
  lampbrush, 100
  maps, 104
Clostridium Pasteurianum, 50
Cnidaria, 145
Coleoptile, experiments with, 179–180, 182
Colonial organisms, *see* Organism
Compounds, 34, 35
Compositae, 160
Compsognatus, 162
Conditional reflexes, 194, 195
  in Pavlov's dogs, 199–200
Conrad-Martius, Hedwig, 17, 88, 121, 142, 143
Consciousness, in everything, 171
Co-ordination, and wholeness, 221
Corticotrophin, 183
Crabs, 190
Crossing-over, 104
Crustacea (crustaceous), 157, 158, 172
Cytaria, 93
Cytoplasm, 93, 97, 98, 100, 101, 103, 110, 112
  and genes, 106
  as function of cell, 96–102
  polarity of with nucleus, 101
  relation to nucleus, 84, 110, 112, 132

Dahl, 156
Dandelion seeds, 171
Darwin, C., 75, 76, 79, 160
Darwinism, 73
Das Werden der Organismen, O. Hertwig's, 79

Decline of the West, Spengler's, 220
Democritus, 11, 13, 15, 66
Deoxyribonucleic acid (DNA), 100, 105
Desmolases, 64
Determinants, 77, 84, 128
Development, 214
Developmental mechanics, 78
Dialectic, in biology, xiii, xiv
Die Grenzen der naturwissenschaftlichen Begriffsbildung, Rickert's, 213
Division of labour, in organisms, 117
Dogs, Pavlov's experiments on, 199–200
Driesch, Hans, 15, 16, 17, 18, 20, 21, 22, 26, 31, 72, 76, 79, 80, 81, 82, 83, 85, 87, 88, 113, 114, 128, 129, 133, 144, 161, 221, 223, 224
and wholeness, 216, 217, 218
entelechial wholeness theory of, 79–85, 215
opposed to Spemann, 126
Drosophila melanogaster, xiii, 104, 160
Dualism, 10, 18, 22
in reaction system, 176
Dujardin, 26, 91
Dürken, 18

Ecological adaptation, *see* Adaptation
Ecology, 153, 156, 158, 171, 219
factors, 173
place relationship, 210, 220
Egg, *see* Cell
"Egomorphism", 151, 165
Ehrenberg, 91
Eimeria gadi, 100
Einstein's, relativity theory, 14
Electrons, 36, 37, 40, 42, 44, 218
Elements, 22, 23, 24, 25
Elliott, 159
Embryo, 80, 82, 83, 121
field, Gurwitsch's theory of, 88
Endocrine gland, 169
Energy, 14, 15, 51, 52, 53, 54, 55, 56, 59, 65, 66
and life, 49–54
conservation of, 68
Ent-harmony, 209, 212

Entelechial wholeness factor, Driesch's, 79–85, 215
Entelechy, 24, 85, 88, 113, 114, 129, 142, 143, 145, 146, 147, 212, 219
and *forma corporis*, 147
and wholeness not identical, 115, 216
cellular, 144
formative, 17, 144
meaning of, 146–7
of cell, 144
of metabiont, 143, 144
relation of whole and part to, 145–146
Environment (*and see* Biotope), 157, 173, 203, 211, 219
and temperature, 155–6
relation to organisms, 154, 208, 209
Enzymes, 29, 44, 53, 60, 63, 64, 65, 94
Eph-harmony, 209, 212
Epigenesis (theories of heredity), 78–90
Essence, 32
Etiology, 156
Euchromatin, 99
Euglena gracilis, 98, 124
Euphorbiaceae, 157, 163
Evolution, theory, 158, 161, 212
Experiential actions, 194–201, 204
Eye, transplantation of, 86

Fabre, 189
Factor-analysis, 152
Falcon, 192
Fertilization, 101
Feulgen's reagent, 99, 100
Field of determination, Weiss', 88
Fischer, Emil, 25
Fish, 154, 158, 163, 173, 219, 220
Flagella, 100
Flagellata, 118, 136, 160
Flight, instinct in birds, 191–3
Flower, development and length of day, 172
Form (*and see* Morphe), 9, 16, 11, 12, 13, 22, 23, 149, 150, 195, 208, 209, 217, 223
action (*Formhandlung*), 176
and adaptation, 170–4
and environment, 153

Form—*contd.*
 and metabiont, 126–32, 143
 elements, 97, 143
 entelechial, 113
 expression of adaptation, 162–4
 forma cellulae, 109
 forma corporis, and entelechy, 147, 216
 goal of living things, 224
 hierarchical order of organic form, 141–8
 kinds of, 113
 life (*Lebensform*), 156
 Linser's (*Zeitgestalt*), 30, 31
 of cell, 109
 problem, 72, conclusions on, 147–148
 space, 112, 131, 134–40, 210, 224
 substantial, 11, 12, 13, 22, 23
 time, 113, 114, 122, 134–40, 135, 136, 210, 224
Forma corporis, and entelechy, 147, 216
 as final cause, 221–4
Formhandlung, 176
Frisch, 196
Frog, 156, 157, 186, 190, 226, 227
 experiments with, 144–5
 Tree, *see* Tree-frog
Function circle, 204

Gabriel, L., 4, 7
Galileo, xii, 6
Galls, 225
Gastrula (gastrulation), 82, 83, 85, 87, 90, 130
 and cell size, 133
Generalization, xii
Genes, 32, 99, 110, 218
 and characteristics of organisms, 105, 106, 107
 and cytoplasm, 106
 and genom, 102–8
 and life, 58, 59
 as catalysts, 108
 in phages, 94
 linked, 103–4
 localized in chromosomes, 104
 nature of, 105
 position effect of, 105
 sequence on chromosomes, 104
 ultimate elements of life, 102

Genom, 143, 160, 203
 and genes, 102–8
 and merogonous systems, 106, 107
Geotropism, 178–9
Germ cells, 103
Germinal layers, 80
Germplasm, 73–8, 88, 160
Giersberg, 177
Gradient theory, of Boveri and Child, 89–90
Granulum, Altmann's, 52
Gredt, 12
Gregarinidea, 122
Grey geese, 188, 199
Gruber, experiments on *Stentor*, 111–112, 114
Guillermond, 99
Gurwitsch, theory of embryo field, 88

Haeckel, 73, 93, 95
Hartmann, M., xii, xiii, 22, 29, 83, 97, 114
Hartmann, N., 94
Hawk, 192
Heintel, E., xiv, 18
Herbst, 78
Hertwig, O., 74
Hertwig, R., 110
Hesse, P., 162, 209
Heteroauxin, *see* Auxin
Heterochromatin, 99
Hertz, 196
Hoerstadius, 89
Hologenous principle (system), 16, 31, 33, 37, 38, 39
 and merogenous correlation, 136
 and wholeness, 70–1, 113, 215, 217
 definition of, 21
 merogenously constituted, 20–1
Holtfreter, 86
Hormones, 29, 169, 175, 177, 180, 185
 and reflex actions, 185
 reactions, 177–84, 194
Horse, 197
Hume, David, 2
Huxley, T. H., 89
Huzella, 58, 143
Hydrolases, 63
Hylidae (tree-frogs), 156–7, 226
Hylomorphism, 11–13

Hypercytaria, 94
Hypophysis, of vertebrates, 183

Immanence, 213–15
India, 157
-indolylacetic acid (IAA), *see* Auxin
Induction, xii, 131
of organs, 85–8
Inert gases, 39, 40, 43
Infusoria, 26, 91, 101, 111
Innate schema, 192, 193, 198, 199,
200, 202
Instability, *see* Stability
Instinctive actions, 187–94, 195, 196,
197, 201, 204, 211
Integral Logic, Leo Gabriel's, 7
Intelligent action, 201–6
Intestinal worms, 49
Invertebrates, 202
Irritability, 9, 117, 150

Jordan, Pasqual, 18

K-shell, 40
Kant, 216–17
Karyolymph, 97
Kestrel, 192
Kekulé, 25
Klebs, 101
Knight, 178
Kochler, O., experiments with
pigeons, 196–7
Köhler, W., 202, 205
Kubiëna, 219
Kühn, 83
Kühnelt, 156, 157, 226

L-shell, 42, 43
Lactuca scariola, 181
Lamarck, J. B. de (Lamarckism),
158, 159, 160
Laws (of nature), 3, 4, 7, 27, 34, 35,
36, 38, 62, 67, 69, 70, 109
a single system in organisms, 212
and organisms, 209
of coaction, 65
of conservation, 68
of co-ordination, 162
of life, different from physical
laws, 210, 211
of place-relationship, 210

of probability, 48
of succession, 68
Mendelian, 78
Lebensform, 156
Leucoplasts, 98
Life (living systems), 1, 8, 9, 10, 11,
13, 14, 15, 18, 19, 21, 22, 23, 28,
46, 57, 58, 102, 109, 142
a hologenous system, 70–1
a physico-chemical process, 59–60
and catalysts, 57–8
and dialectic, 18
and energy, 49–54, 59
and genes, 58
and growth and decay, 54–6
and mechanism, 57, 58, 59, 60
and order, 56
and oxygen, 49–50
and stability, 68
animate and inanimate systems,
46–71, 210–11
cell, unit of, 92
definition of, 33, 57
does not arise *de novo*, 110
explanation of, 32
force, 24, 25
function of cell, 57
nature and origins of, 47–9, 92
not isolated, 9
ordered relationship, 208–27
parts in organism, 57–62
phenomenon, unique, 209
physical unit of, 25–6, 91
uniqueness of, 209
Lillie, 128, 129
Linaria cymbalaria, 181
Linser, Hans, 29, 30, 31, 32, 33, 34,
44, 59, 121
Lion, 197
Lipoid, 58
Locomotive component of cell, 97
Lorenz, 186, 187, 188, 189, 192, 198,
199, 201
Lysenko, 74

M-shell, 42, 43
Macrocosm (ic), 35, 36, 37
Malaya, 157
Mammals, 163
Mangold, Hilda, 86
March, 70, 215

Materia (*prima, signata*), 11, 12, 67, 147, 148
Materialism, 23, 74
Matter, 8, 10, 11, 12, 13, 14, 23, 62, 69, 141
  animate different from inanimate, 209–11
Mechanism (theory), mechanists, 8, 10–45, 47, 53, 64, 66, 67, 69, 73, 74, 76, 79
  and life, 57–8, 59, 60
  explanation of reflexes, 186–7
  point of view, 213
Meiosis (reduction division), 103, 104
Mendel, G., 103
Mendelian laws, xiii
Merogenous principle (system), 15, 27, 31, 32, 33, 34, 36, 37, 38, 39, 44, 45, 67, 70, 108, 134, 139, 225
  and cell state, 121–6
  and genes, 106
  and metabionts, 126
  and purposiveness of hologenous system, 136
  and stability, 56
  and wholeness, 215, 217
  definition of, 20
  in hologenous systems, 20–1
Metabionts, 116–48, 176, 219
  a colony of cells, 126
  and form, 126–32
  as a unit, 126–41
  cells of, homologous with protista, 126
  cells not different from protista cells, 122–3
  entelechy of, 143
  forma corporis of, 148
  no correspondence with protist cell, 145
  protist colonies, 118–20
  relation of metabiont to protista, 116–26
  space and time form of, 134–40
  wholeness of, 136, 211
Metabolism, 9, 49, 52, 54, 58, 59, 93, 102, 117, 150, 211
Meyer-Abich, 215
Micells, 33, 52, 59, 93, 210
Microcosm (ic), 35, 36, 37, 40
Mirabilis jalapa, xiii
Mitochondria, 98

Mitosis, *see* Cell division
Mittasch, 18, 19, 20, 44
Mitterer, 12
Moewus, 125
Molecules, 17, 18, 19, 20, 21, 23, 27, 28, 29, 32, 37, 38, 39, 40, 43, 44, 47, 48, 49, 59, 60, 61, 62, 63, 66, 67, 69, 70, 107, 108, 110, 113, 114, 141, 143, 157, 164, 203, 209, 210, 211, 212, 213
  and genes, 103
  and order, 62, 142–3
Morgan, Lloyd, 187
Morgan, T. H., 78
Morphe (*and see* Form), 153, 209, 210, 211, 212
Morphogenesis (morphology), 16, 18, 21, 72–3, 78, 81, 88, 91, 150, 173, 212
  and wholeness, 139–40
  of cell, 123–6
Mosaic ova, 84, 129
Mosaic theory, of Roux and Weismann, 76, 77, 78, 80, 83
Moyse, Alexis, 17, 18, 110, 211
Mucoraceae, 176
Muller, Johann, 23
Mutations (theory), 104, 159, 160
  of phages, 94

Nägeli, 52, 93
Natural science, and philosophical terms, 214–15
Nematoda, 145
Neo-Lamarckians, 75
Neuberg, 18
Nicotiana, 139, 140
Norms of reaction, 175–206
Nuclear spindle, 97
Nucleic acid, 95, 96, 100
Nucleoprotein, 95, 96, 99, 100, 218
Nucleus, 28, 33, 35, 36, 37, 40, 42, 74, 75, 76, 93, 97, 98, 99, 100, 101, 103, 110, 112, 116, 143
  function of cell, 96
  lacking in blue-green algae, 96
  of *Stentor*, 111, 112
  polarity of with cytoplasm, 101
  relation to cytoplasm, 84, 110, 112, 132
  sap, 97

Octet rule, 43
Optic cup, and development of egg, 86
Order, 4, 13, 15, 56, 62–6, 69, 70, 71, 109, 110, 120, 134, 135
and living systems, 60, 63, 64, 227
and reactions, 208–9
causal, 149–53
for wholeness in plants, 139–40
for wholeness in sponges, 138
hierarchy of organic form, 141–8
imposition of, 137–40
in metabionts, 132
in molecules and cells, 142–3
not identical with material substratum, 65–6
of cell, 109, 218
principles of, 63–4, 65, 85, 112
transcendence, 147
Ordo naturae, as end causality, 224–227
Organism (animate), 15, 16, 17, 20, 23, 26, 28, 29–33, 45, 49, 61, 67, 75, 85, 91, 135, 150, 157, 163, 164, 167, 169, 173, 208, 210, 211, 213, 214, 221
a hologenous system, 70–1
and adaptations, 153–62
and genoms, 107–8
and living parts, 57–62
and purposiveness, 209
and reactivity, 165–6
and use of oxygen, 49–50
colonial, 118–19
definition of, 30
euryphagous, 155–6
form, goal of, 224
in biology, 213
metabiont, a colony of cells, 126
relation of protista to metabiont, 116–26
relation to environment, 154–5
stenophagous, 155–6
the multicellular, 116–48
wholeness, 224
Organizers, 131
and induction of organs, 85–8
Ovum, _see_ Cell, egg

Paramecium, 151, 175
Parthenogenesis, 74
Pascher, 118

Pasteur, 92
Pavlov, 171, 194, 195, 198, 199–200
Pelomyxa palustris, 95
Perception in biology, 1–4
Peregrine falcon, 191, 192
Periodic table, 40, 41
Pflanzen-physiologie, Boysen-Jensen's, 139
Pflüger, 46, 47
Phenomena, biological, 28
explanation of, 27–9
Phototropism, in plants, 178–82, 207
Phylogenetic regulation, 158
Phyloscopus sibillatrix, 154
Physiology, 151, 152, 170, 171, 172, 173, 183, 188, 190
of stimulation, 164–70, 172, 186
Piekarski, 95
Pigeons, Koehler's, 196–7
Pilobolus crystallinus, 176–7, 180
Pituitary gland, 183
Plastic actions, 187, 195–8, 204–5
Plastids, 98, 101
Pluripotency, concept of, 128
Pluteus, 222
Polyp, 145
Position effect of gene, 105
Positivism (positivist), 2, 3, 7, 153
Potentiality (factors), 81, 82, 83, 84, 85, 88, 108, 129, 134, 138, 139, 145, 151, 160, 172, 205, 214, 221
and environment, 158
and hormones, 183
and instinctive actions, 187
of developing egg cells, 123–6, 128, 129, 130, 131, 132
Preyer, 92
Primeval slime, Haeckel's, 93, 95
Privatio, in multicellular organisms, 116
of substantial form, 12
Probability, 36, 48, 104
Proteins, 100
Proteus, 223
Protista, 116, 117, 118, 121, 124, 135, 145, 167, 175
cell, no correspondence with metabiont, 145
development of, and egg compared, 126–7
Protocytaria, 93
Protoplasmic reactions, 175–7

Protozoa, 26, 91, 96, 111, 176
Psychism, 217
Psychology, 151, 152
Purpose (purposiveness, teleology), 17, 64, 66, 68, 69, 70, 71, 135, 174, 210, 214, 217, 221, 225
  and adaptations, 158–9
  and instincts, 193–4
  and reactions, 208–9
  in hologenous and merogenous systems, 136
  in metabionts, 132–4

Racophorus, 226
Ranidae, 157, 226
Rats, 188
Reactivity (reaction), and adaptation, 149–74, 212
  and purposiveness, 208–9
  experiential, 194–201, 204
  escape, 191
  hormonal, 177–84, 185, 194
  instinctive, 187–94, 195, 196, 197, 201, 204
  intelligent, 201–6
  norms of, 175–206
  of external organisms, 165–6
  plastic, 187, 195–8
  protoplasmic, 175–7
  reflex, 184–7, 189–90, 191, 194, 195, 196, 201
  system, dualism in, 176
  summing-up, 209
Redstart, the, 155
Reduction division, *see* Meiosis
Reflex actions, 171, 184–7, 191, 194, 195, 196, 201, 211
  relation to instinct, 189–90
Regulation ova, 129
Reichenow, 96
Regularity, in science, 3–8
Reptiles, colour in, 5
Reserve plasm, Weiss's, 88
Respiration, 49–54, 55, 66
Richter, 92
Rickert, 67, 213
Ribonucleic acid (RNA), 100
Riehl, A., xii
Rohracher, 200
Root, tropisms of, 178
Rotatoria, 145
Roux, 76, 78, 84

Salamander, 83, 100, 144
Sarcodic material, 91
Schaffer, 58
Schleiden, 25, 57, 91
Schlick, Moritz, 15, 34, 35, 36, 40
Schrödinger, E., 102
Schwann, 25, 57, 91
Sea-urchin, 91, 132
  Boveri's experiments on, 132–3
  Driesch's experiments on, 80
  Hoerstadius's experiments on, 89
Seals, 173
Shoot, tropisms of, 178
Siebold, von, 26
Somatic cells, *see* Cell
Somatoplasm, 76
Somatotrophin, 183
Space-form, 113
Spann, Othmar, 220
Sparrow, 208
Sparrowhawk, 191, 192
Spemann, 17, 21, 82, 83, 89, 90, 121, 123, 124, 144
  induction and organizer, 85–8
  opposed to Driesch, 126
Spencer, 187
Spengler, 220
Spermatozoon (sperms), 75, 101
Spirogyra, 101
Sponge, 145
  experiments on, 137–8
Sporozoa, 122
Stability (and instability), 40, 43, 46, 47, 56, 61, 62, 63, 65, 68, 149, 210
  and inanimate wholes, 36–43
  and living things, 56, 61
  factor of, 61, 62
Statoliths (organs), 184, 190
Stentor, 111–12, 114, 222
Stimuli (stimulation), 149, 152, 166, 168, 169, 175, 177, 178, 185, 190, 208, 212
  biological relevance of, 170–4
  definition, 168, 169
  physiology of, 151, 152, 164–70, 172, 173, 186
Stolte, experiments on *Stentor*, 112
Storch, O., 93–4, 203
Strasburger, 74
Subjectivism, 68
Swift, 155

Teleology, *see* Purposiveness
Temperature, and environment, 155–156
Time factor, in development, 83
Time-form, *see* Form
Timofeeff-Ressovsky, 161
Toad, 157
Transcendence, 213–15
Transplantation experiments, 82, 83, 85–8
Tree-frog (Hylidae), 156–7
Tropisms, 176–80
Trypanosomes, 100
Turkish duck, 199

Uexküll, J. von, 16, 141, 142, 143, 161, 171, 175, 176
Unity, *see* Wholeness
Urea, synthesis of, 24–5

Variations, 6, 75, 150
Vertebrates, 57, 145, 162
  hypophysis, 183
Verworn, Max, 46, 47, 52, 58, 93
Viruses, 93, 94, 95, 99, 101, 102, 108
Vitalism (theory, vitalist), 8, 10–45, 47, 66, 67, 68, 72
  explanation of reflexes, 186–7
  point of view, 213
Vogt, 129

Warburg, 53
Wasps, 225, 226
Weinland, 49, 50
Weismann, 72, 74, 75, 76, 77, 78, 80, 81, 82, 83, 84, 85, 88, 128, 160
  germ-plasm theory, 73–8
Weiss, P., 88

Wenzl, Aloys, 218
Whales, 173
What is Life?, Schrödingers's, 102
Wholeness (wholes, unity), 15, 16, 17, 19, 20, 21, 22, 33, 36–43, 44, 109, 214, 215–21, 223
  and analysis, 183–4
  and Kant, 216–17
  and organisms, 224
  biodynamic, 66–71, 210
  both aim and cause, 70, 224
  contrasted in living and inanimate systems, 223
  Driesch's entelechial factor of, 79–85
  factor, 81, 82, 84, 85, 113
  in individual cells, 120–1
  in living processes, 209–12
  in sponges, 137–8
  merogenous and hologenous, 215
  not applicable to life only, 223
  of metabiont, 119–20, 136
  principles of, 70–1, 113, 137–40
  sum of reactions, 209
Wilson, 78, 83
Winogradsky, 50
Wolff, Gustav, 16, 17, 18, 134, 221, 222, 224
Woltereck, 142
Wöhler, 24, 26

Xanthophyll, 98

Yeast, 50

Zeitgestalt, 30
Ziegler, 189
Zierlursachlich, 221
Zumstein, 98
Zygote, 103